STACKED *with* FLAVOR

An Anti-Inflammatory Cookbook With Dairy-Free, Grain-Free & Low-Sugar Recipes

BY SHAWNA CORONADO

1503 S.W. 42nd St.
Topeka, KS 66609-1265, USA
Telephone: (785) 274-4300
Fax: (785) 274-4305
www.ogdenpubs.com

Text © 2019 Shawna Coronado
Photography © 2019 Shawna Coronado
Illustrations © 2019 Kelsey Lee Connors, Pages 26, 40, 179
Pixabay images: Pages 8, 9, 10, 14, 15, 16, 178

Publisher: Bill Uhler
Editorial Director: Oscar H. Will III
Merchandise and Event Director: Andrew Perkins
Production Director: Bob Cucciniello
Special Content Editorial Director: Christian Williams
Special Content Group Editor: Jean Teller
Special Content Assistant Editors: Ashley Hannen, Eli Hoelscher
Book Design and Layout: Alex Tatro

Ogden Publications titles are also available for retail, wholesale, promotional, and bulk purchase. For details, contact Customer Service: (800) 234-3368; customerservice@ogdenpubs.com; or Ogden Publications, Inc., 1503 S.W. 42nd St., Topeka, Kansas 66609-1265.

ISBN: 978-1-948734-07-3

This book is dedicated to
my wonderful family.
I love you.
I am grateful for you.
You mean everything to me.

IMPORTANT NOTE TO MY DEAR READERS:

This book is not intended to replace the advice of a physician, nutritionist,
health-care professional, or medical practitioner.

The information and recipes in this book are for educational purposes only. See your
health-care provider before beginning any new health, food, or diet program, particularly if
you are pregnant, lactating, or have a complex medical condition. The author and publisher
specifically disclaim all responsibility for any liability, loss, or risk, personal or otherwise, incurred
as a consequence, directly or indirectly, of the use and application of any content of this book.

Choosing an expert who practices Integrative Functional Nutrition (IFN) is a great way to
get started on sound nutritional lifestyle choices. Consult with them often to discuss your
progress. Stick with your plan—eat well and live a wellness lifestyle—I believe in you!

When I was diagnosed with severe degenerative osteoarthritis of the spine in 2015, the pain was so great I could barely walk or sleep. Devastated, I thought my life was over. Discovering that healthy food choices can reduce chronic inflammatory pain changed my pain levels and my life forever. While on my anti-inflammatory food plan, I went from barely walking to walking between three and five miles every day, with almost 80 percent less pain than when I was first diagnosed. I found my health and have my life back.

Having had this traumatic life experience, my heartfelt mission is to now help others reclaim their health, life, and happiness. More than a cookbook filled with recipes, this guide to reducing chronic inflammation can help you take a positive step toward a personalized wellness lifestyle that will, hopefully, bring you pain relief and improved health.

—Shawna Coronado

TABLE OF CONTENTS

INTRODUCTION

WHAT IS CHRONIC INFLAMMATION AND HOW IS IT CONNECTED TO FOOD?

Let's say you are diagnosed with diabetes, heart disease, high blood pressure, arthritis, asthma, or any inflammatory disease that compromises your health and might be causing you chronic pain. The doctor put you on a restrictive diet that tastes like cardboard. You feel resentful, of course, and as if you have no power over your food and your life. Within a few weeks you return to your old way of eating out of frustration and lack of helpful guidance. My goal is to help you feel better and live a better lifestyle by discovering a smart anti-inflammatory food plan *full of flavor* and by showing you how to stick with it.

Believe me, I understand how you feel. My chronic pain was so severe I could barely walk, and, while I truly believe food is the cure, I also know bland diets were holding me back. I discovered how to add so much flavor and variety to my daily food plan with herbs, spices, and cooking techniques that I now love cooking and eating. My health conditions made a powerful turnaround, with many of my issues—like high blood pressure—disappearing entirely. This book is the result of my discovering the foods and techniques that brought flavor to the foreground in my own diet. It all started with my diagnosis. ...

A STORY OF PAIN AND RECOVERY WITH FOOD & EXERCISE

Being diagnosed with severe degenerative osteoarthritis of the spine—and all the accompanying pain, seclusion, and sadness that went with it—helped spiral me down emotionally to the point I felt my life was over. Pain is an isolator, and I felt alone and frustrated, unable to heal or recover in a way that would lessen my pain.

When I went to the doctor, I felt sure my problem would be muscle-related. I was shocked when I was diagnosed with severe osteoarthritis, also known as degenerative joint disease; I wasn't yet 50 years old. No cure exists for this condition as, essentially, the material between the vertebrae of my spine has disintegrated, causing permanent malformation and intense pain from bone rubbing against bone. While my doctor insisted I start prescription pain therapy—opioids and others—as part of my treatment, I asked for alternatives. He recommended walking and physical therapy; however, he had no other ideas beyond surgery or prescriptions. I truly wanted a scientifically proven alternative to all the expense, drama, and addiction concerns of opioid-level pain medications.

Consulting with Deepa Deshmukh, MPH, RD, LDN, BC-ADM, a clinical nutritionist practicing Integrative Functional Nutrition (IFN), really changed my outlook. First, she became my nutritional food guide and helped me understand what chronic inflammation is and how it affects the body, then helped me discover a food plan designed to improve the inflammation related to my specific condition. Along with her nutritional advice, I also incorporated an exercise plan, which truly upped my wellness goals and helped reduce my pain significantly.

WHAT IS CHRONIC INFLAMMATION?

Chronic inflammation is more than a pain response, it is an important part of our immune system. Basically, inflammation is the body's physiological response to injury. If you are injured or have an infection, sentinel cells alert your immune system to the problem, sending signals to other cells within your body to help defend against foreign invaders and repair injury. This causes an inflammatory response. Heat, pain, redness, swelling, and loss of function are all signs of an acute inflammatory reaction. When the injury is healed, the inflammation goes away.

A prolonged response is known as chronic inflammation. With persistent chronic inflammation, there may be no specific injury such as a cut or pulled muscle, yet the inflammatory response continues throughout the body. This repetitive distress reaction can lead to a variety of chronic inflammatory diseases. Included in this list are diabetes, arthritis and joint disease, cardiovascular disease, allergies, asthma, fibromyalgia, chronic obstructive pulmonary disease (COPD), HIV, Crohn's disease, lupus, and many others. According to the National Cancer Institute "people with chronic inflammatory bowel diseases, such as ulcerative colitis and Crohn's disease, have an increased risk of colon cancer. ... Over time, chronic inflammation can cause DNA damage and lead to cancer."

Currently, various causes are blamed for chronic low-grade inflammation: consistent and high stress, sleep deprivation, poor fitness, secondary illness or infection, obesity, aging, poor diet, and addictions such as those to sugar, drugs, alcohol, and nicotine. Yet scientists do not fully understand what specifically causes chronic inflammation, so the research continues. It is important to note that many of these conditions are preventable as they are created by lifestyle choices. Research has proven that exercising, reducing addictive substances, and, most importantly, improving the diet, can significantly reduce a body's reactivity to a chronically inflamed state.

Keeping chronic inflammation and its byproducts—disease and chronic inflammatory pain—at bay is assisted by smart anti-inflammatory lifestyle choices, such as exercising more and improving the diet.

HOW I FIGHT CHRONIC INFLAMMATION WITHOUT MEDICATIONS

I have heard it said that life begins at the end of your comfort zone. My particular comfort zone involved only occasional—or summer seasonal—exercise and a diet rife with sugar. Without a doubt, sugar has been my nemesis, and it was a challenging addiction to break, so I understand how changing your food routine might seem uncomfortable. Walking daily and following the food plan my nutritionist prescribed was way beyond my comfort zone, yet when my osteoarthritis caused such extreme pain, I could not function. Moving beyond my emotional comfort zone was absolutely necessary in order to find my health.

You too might have to move beyond your comfort zone. People have told me, "It's too hard to give up dairy!" Really? It's too difficult to give up a few simple foods in order to reduce your inflammatory pain? In my opinion, losing an arm or a leg is difficult or climbing a mountain is difficult. Eliminating dairy products from your life and adding fresh delicious foods are simply new habits. It is not hard, particularly if it eliminates disease and extends your life, brings you many additional years of joy with your loved ones, and reduces chronic pain. My life has changed enormously because I was willing to make a sacrifice or two. By making these changes, I have gained so much more by lowering my chronic pain and increasing my quality of life. You can experience this too.

HOW MY HEALTH CHANGED

Essentially, the focus of my particular anti-inflammatory food regimen is no dairy, no grains, and low natural sugars. My nutritionist and I set a 60-day trial run, and I tracked what I ate with an online tracking device to help me build a better understanding of what my daily habits and needs might be. Within four days of going on the food plan, my inflammatory pain was reduced by about 40 percent and I was sleeping again. At the end of 30 days, I went off the high blood pressure medication I had been taking for 15 years. By day 60, I felt better than I had in years, and my pain had receded so significantly, I committed to the food plan for the rest of that year.

In another six months, my daily inflammatory pain had lessened from the day I was diagnosed by about 80 percent. Even more significantly, my severe allergies receded; I went from my yearly three or four sinus infections to no infections and no bronchitis, and to minimal reactions to my usual allergens. Since then, I have remained on the food plan for more than four years, and I feel better than ever. Working with my nutritionist and dedicating myself to a new wellness lifestyle has truly changed my life for the better.

WALK, WALK, WALK!

To be clear, a healthier diet is not enough to effect all the changes you might want in your search for better health. With this in mind, I walk at least one hour every day I am able. If it is too cold or hot to walk outside, I walk in malls, supercenters, and on indoor tracks. I found that a food plan only goes so far, as it must absolutely be accompanied by walking or some other form of exercise. If you do no other workout, at the bare minimum, walk daily. With the permission of your medical professionals, walking or another low-impact exercise needs to be the foundational goal you shoot for to keep your system moving and to kick your food plan into gear. Your blood is pumping, your joints are liquid, your gut is stimulated, and your energy level is up when you walk daily. This contributes immensely to helping you stay uplifted and motivated to continue your food plan.

Discovering other forms of doctor-approved exercise that might increase your strength capabilities, extend your joint range, and prevent further deterioration brought on by chronic inflammation can also help. Yoga is a great tool to help you renew strength and extend your flexibility; below you see my dear friends Jenny Nybro Peterson, Terri Curtis, and Jacque Gregory during a yoga session at Jenny's amazing Berkeley Farm in Austin, Texas. Other low-impact exercises include walking, rowing, swimming, tai chi, dancing, cycling, and strength training. Gardening helps you build muscle strength and also keeps you outdoors in the sunshine, another mood-lifting activity.

ONE SIZE DOES NOT FIT ALL

This anti-inflammatory lifestyle is not about weight loss and it is not a diet designed for weight loss. The food plan and recipes described in this book are tools to help you reduce systemic inflammation and chronic pain, much as I have done. With a positive food plan, you will feel better every day of your life by lowering your body's inflammation.

Perhaps you have tried one of the many popular whole-food meal plans that are high in fresh produce and low in red meat, sugar, and saturated fat such as the Mediterranean Diet, Mayo Clinic Diet, TLC (Therapeutic Lifestyle Changes) diet, or Dr. Weil's Anti-Inflammatory Diet. While these plans may help you with weight loss, they also have the more important goals of increasing your wellness and reducing chronic health problems.

Each diet or meal plan is a bit different: There is no one-size-fits-all that works for every person on the planet. Increasing health and wellness are the goals with my specific anti-inflammatory dietary plan; my aim is to feel better and live a wellness lifestyle to help reduce negative health issues. This book is filled with recipes that will work with the above diet plans or with a customized meal plan you create, with the help of this book and your health professionals, in order to achieve your lower inflammation goals. In fact, the recipes in this book are meant to complement the majority of these nutritionally sound, doctor- or health-care professional-recommended diet plans.

EXTREME FOOD PLANS ARE NOT HEALTHY

It is important to connect with a health-care professional such as a doctor or nutritionist who understands and is accredited in Integrative Functional Nutrition (IFN). These professionals can craft an IFN recommended food plan with sound nutritional choices, all aimed at helping you restore physiological functioning of the body.

This healthy expert-guided food plan approach is absolutely not an "extreme diet" or "fad diet" that will starve your body of fiber and nutrition. Extreme diets, the type that require you to eat only one type of food for 10 days, or completely eliminate fat or plant protein, or restrict your caloric intake to extreme lows, for example, may have extreme detrimental consequences on your health, particularly when conducted without medical supervision.

Yo-yo dieting between plans also can cause intense health problems. Eating a consistently healthy meal plan as a lifestyle choice is the key to success. Building a smart anti-inflammatory food plan is a lifestyle change that can help you feel better for the rest of your life; it eliminates inflammatory foods that might trigger reactions and features an abundance of plant-based whole foods and lean meat or other protein sources.

HOW TO DISCOVER YOUR FOOD TRIGGERS AND WHAT FOODS SHOULD YOU EAT?

Medically sound advice should rise above the fake news that is currently rampant within the anti-inflammatory food industry. Scientific research has indicated saturated fat and high-cholesterol foods are more highly inflammatory than previously thought. Research also shows that fiber is important to a diet, and high fiber foods score much lower on the inflammatory scale. Whole plant-based foods have higher fiber and more nutrition, so they become a smart choice in a wellness centered diet. Cardiologists recommend a Mediterranean-type diet. This food plan includes vegetables, herbs, olive oil, whole grains, fresh chicken, and fresh fish, and it is also light on ultra-processed foods and red meat.

Adjusting your diet to address the inflammation in your body is not just about eating "miracle foods" to help trigger a positive response in your system. Reducing inflammation with food can happen if you eliminate the processed foods, the excess saturated fat and oils, the poor dietary choices, and the poor daily exercise choices that generate and hold long-term chronic inflammation in your body. While there is a lot of hype about certain herbs or spices being miracle cures, there is no one miracle food or miracle pill that can completely and instantaneously reduce your inflammation. Inflammatory food responses are extremely individualized and might be caused by a food intolerance or an allergy issue, not simply a specific food. The only way to see if you have a reaction to a particular food item—a food intolerance or allergen sensitivity—is to eliminate it from your diet, then gradually reintroduce it to test your reactions.

TEMPORARILY ELIMINATING REACTIONARY FOODS

My nutritionist suggested I eliminate certain foods for 30 to 60 days, then reintroduce them individually to see how I responded. These foods included dairy, grains, beans/legumes, and processed sugars along with crustacean shellfish, peanuts, and soybeans. This is not to suggest that I am allergic to these things; by eliminating these items I gave my body time to recover from food intolerances and to give myself time to better understand what triggers inflammatory responses in my system.

Once a strict 30 to 60 days of eating a clean diet have passed, then it is time to gradually reintroduce foods to test your reactions. Nutritionists recommend waiting a minimum of four days before introducing a new food. Therefore, once you pass the initial 30 days, try a new food, wait four days to gauge your body's reaction, and then introduce another new food.

Do you have pain, asthma, sinusitis, upper respiratory issues, swelling, heartburn, soreness, migraine headaches, diarrhea, gas, constipation, bloating, skin rash, or another more immediate reaction? Listen to your body and consult with your health professional if needed. Soon you will determine what foods are triggering your chronic inflammation. I, for instance, can have ghee but I do not do well with cheese or other dairy. I react severely to soy and beans, but I can have tree nuts without any problems. Perhaps your triggers will be completely different than mine. Once you begin, you will be surprised at how much food truly affects your body, and you will rejoice in the newfound ability to reduce some of your inflammatory pain and other problems without the use of prescription drugs.

ANTI-INFLAMMATORY FOODS ARE WHOLE FOODS

Breaking lifetime habits and restarting a food plan can be challenging. However, the reward for my food plan efforts has been immense for me personally as I am now able to sleep better, walk three miles daily, and live with considerably fewer allergy and pain issues. This is all thanks to my nutritionist working with me to customize an anti-inflammatory food plan that makes sense for my body.

What follows is a guide list of the anti-inflammatory foods I use to lower my pain. (In Chapter 16, you will find a full meal guide to help you build customized anti-inflammatory meal plans with the help of the recipes in this book.) You will, of course, need to modify these foods based on your own dietary and medical needs, which you can coordinate with your health-care professional.

WHY EAT WHOLE FOODS?

Current scientific research continues to suggest a fiber-filled diet rich in whole plant-based foods is the most healthful. A whole food is defined as a food that has not been heavily refined or processed, and, most importantly, the food is free from preservatives, additives, and other artificial substances. In other words, food that has been altered significantly from its natural form during a manufacturing process is likely to be lower in fiber and nutrients and higher in fat and sugar, all of which can trigger inflammation. Of course, we still need to include some processed foods in a modern healthy food plan such as non-dairy milks, vinegars, or cold-pressed oils. Eating packaged whole foods, such as frozen vegetables or whole-grain pastas and breads, is a definite positive if it conforms to the recommendations of your health-care professional.

Becoming a vegan or vegetarian can be a smart way to live an anti-inflammatory food plan through whole-food, plant-based living. It is also possible to eat low-fat animal-based proteins as a part of a more largely plant-based diet in order to find better inflammatory reactions. As mentioned before, the Mediterranean Diet, Mayo Clinic Diet, TLC (Therapeutic Lifestyle Changes) diet, or Dr. Weil's Anti-Inflammatory Diet are healthy choices for a fundamentally plant-based diet that includes some animal-based proteins and offers all the benefits of consuming healthy fats and whole foods. My personal food plan eliminates dairy, which is included in a few of these general diets, because I continue to react to dairy in most forms, and my health-care professionals and I have decided to permanently eliminate such products. Many people have eliminated dairy permanently from their diets as dairy can cause inflammatory reactions in the human body. Watch your physical reactions and follow the advice of your health-care guides to determine what might need to be permanently eliminated from your food plan.

The *Eat This Food* list that follows is a basic outline of healthy, mostly whole foods, all of which are a part of a healthy anti-inflammatory meal plan. When shopping for any foods, be sure to consider organic first; chemical- and additive-free is always best. A general rule to whole-food eating is the fewer ingredients the better. Reading labels for all products is critical so you can eliminate inflammatory chemical-filled ingredients and find products with more healthful components.

WHAT TO EAT AND WHAT NOT TO EAT
PAUSE THIS FOOD TEMPORARILY

Exclude these items for the first 30 to 60 days of a food plan:

- Gluten and grains found in pasta and bread products (ancient grains, buckwheat, corn, millet, oats, quinoa, wheat, wild rice, and all sprouted grains)
- Dairy
- Natural unrefined sugars—honey, maple syrup, and other natural sugars
- Nuts—peanut and tree nut products (excluding coconut and nut milks)
- Soy and soy-based products

After your initial month or two on the plan, gradually reintroduce foods from the above pause list, as recommended by your nutritionist or doctor, to test your reactions.

Reintroduce a single food item once every four days in order to give your body time to absorb and react to each food. Some foods may need to be permanently eliminated as they can cause intense inflammatory reactions in some people. These include soy and dairy, while other food categories will be able to be reintroduced with no problems.

The below food choices all play a healthy part in your everyday food plan and represent whole, minimally processed items:

- Broth—all organic bone, chicken, fish, game, and vegetable broths that have no artificial ingredients added
- Drinks—water is preferred; other drinks include black tea, green tea, herbal tea, coffee, non-dairy no-added-sugar milk, limited sparkling or soda water (it should not replace plain water as your primary drink)
- Healthy fats—avocados, chia seeds, coconut meat, flaxseeds, hemp seeds, tahini, sesame seeds, sunflower seeds, seed butters, and olives
- Flours—all non-grain, non-soy-based flours
- Fruit—low-sugar fruit such as berries, avocados, eggplant, olives, peppers, tomatoes, and a squeeze of lemon/lime for flavorings (dried fruit, pineapple, and other high-sugar fruit should be limited)
- Herbs and spices—all herbs and spices, including cacao and 100-percent cocoa; go light on the salt
- Oils—cold-pressed oils such as extra-virgin olive oil and avocado oil, occasional use of ghee (or butter if your system handles it well), safflower oil, sesame oil, and sunflower oil
- Protein—beans, legumes, seeds, seed butters, chicken/poultry, eggs, fish, fatty fish, game, pork, rabbit, and seafood (avoid other red meats, nitrates, and other additives in processed deli meat and sausage meats)
- Vegetables—all fresh or frozen vegetables, particularly garlic, onions, cruciferous vegetables, sprouts, pea tendrils, microgreens, leafy green vegetables, mushrooms, root vegetable greens, and low-starch root vegetables (radish, jicama, beet, carrot, celeriac, rutabaga, and turnip); limit high starch vegetables
- Vinegar—any form

Enjoy a variety of these foods while you are on the first 30 to 60 days of the plan and into the future. If any of the foods give you an inflammatory reaction of some kind, temporarily eliminate the specific trigger food along with other pause foods in order to confirm which food is causing the problem.

Remember, produce truly is the backbone of every meal; plant-based foods such as fruit and vegetables can make a difference in your recovery. Aim to eat a well-rounded variety of nutritious foods based on vitamin content, fiber, and suggested portion recommendations.

- Artificial colors, sweeteners, preservatives, and additives
- GMO (genetically modified organism) foods
- Artificially sweetened drinks and sodas, high calorie/highly sweetened coffee drinks, as well as all processed sweetened juices, drinks, and sodas (limit beer, wine, and alcohol)
- Foods made with saturated and trans fat, like unclarified butter, deep fried foods, fatty meat, lard, margarine, refined vegetable oils, shortening and other hydrogenated oils, saturated fat oils, and poultry skin (limit red meat with grass-fed beef preferred)
- Non-whole grain products such as sugary cereals, chips, white bread, and crackers
- Cane and other refined sugars, syrups, and high-fructose sweeteners
- Most ketchups, mayonnaise, and salad dressings; they likely contain soy, corn syrups, and other ultra-processed ingredients
- Ultra-processed junk food of all types such as snacks, chips, dips, candies, donuts, and those with high-chemical contents

Bottom line: Ultra-processed foods are filled with chemicals, dozens of added ingredients, and all the junk that might be triggering your inflammatory reactions. Reading labels for all products is critical to consistently eliminate inflammatory ingredients from your diet.

If you read the labels of typical condiments such as ketchup, mayonnaise, jams and jellies, salad dressings, and other jarred sauces, you will see they are ultra-processed and filled with artificial colors, sweeteners, preservatives, and additives. Going organic helps reduce some of these chemicals; however, you can also try eating foods without condiments, enjoying the natural flavors on your plate. Another solution is to make your own condiments, such as salad dressings, with fewer chemicals and ingredients that will not trigger any inflammatory sensitivities.

The previous lists are a smart first-step shopping list for all kinds of yummy food and dishes that are filled with healthful benefits.

Working with your doctor or nutritionist will help narrow down a few categories. For instance, I have been on my anti-inflammatory food plan for more than four years now, but for some reason my body still rejects dairy, grains, and beans. I have tried multiple times to reintroduce these foods without success. I am not disheartened about not having these items in my pantry because *I eat so much food with this food plan that I am never hungry*. It is all about increasing taste.

By using herbs, spices, vinegar, oil, and all the items on the *Eat This Food* list, I feel I have enhanced the taste of food and truly enjoy eating more than I did before. Using your food list, you can add herbs and spices so your meals taste over-the-top great, like gourmet menus, with very little effort. I will show you how with the tips and tricks that follow in upcoming chapters. It is easy to add flavor and still have a healthful diet, and, of course, that is what the recipes in this book are all about. Cooking the foods on your particular food plan to retain flavor and deliciousness is what is going to keep you on your food plan so you can rediscover your wellness.

Another great source of assistance is the *The Wellness Garden Fruit and Vegetables Nutrition Chart* (on Page 20), which can help you decide what vegetables you might like in your diet that have a higher vitamin or lower sugar or carbohydrate content. With this chart as a guide, you can choose which vegetables and fruits to grow in your garden or which specific whole produce to shop for that can more specifically address your medical needs from a nutritional perspective. You can also see which types of produce have a lower sugar content, making those smart choices for your anti-inflammatory food plan.

WILLPOWER TIPS AND HOW TO STAY ON YOUR FOOD PLAN

Now that you are thinking of developing a clever food and meal plan to combat your inflammatory issues, it's time to learn a few creative ways to help you remain dedicated every day to the plan to help you achieve success:

• **Daily Log and Food Tracking Apps**—When I first began my anti-inflammatory food plan, I had a difficult time remembering what I ate every day, so adopting a written daily log or digital food tracker helped me better understand what I was eating daily so I could stick to the plan. This kept me on track with my goals and away from packaged foods by enabling me to view my progress.

• **Fluids**—According to the National Academies of Sciences, Engineering, and Medicine, men should be drinking about 15.5 cups (3.7 liters) and women should be drinking about 11.5 cups (2.7 liters) of fluids every single day. When your tummy grumbles and it is not a set meal or snack time, drink 8 ounces of water first before you snack. We are often thirsty, not hungry, and drinking the recommended daily amount of fluids is very important for your body processes. Water—even broth or unsweetened tea—instead of a sugary snack can go a long way to helping lower your chronic inflammation.

• **Advance Prep**—Pre-preparing your foods via bulk cooking and meal planning can make an immense difference in helping you stick with your plan. When you come home from a long day of work, for instance, and it is 7 p.m. or later, you are tired. It is much easier to grab junk food at this time rather than fix an entire healthful meal. Advance planning enables you to have better portion control, spend less money because cooking in bulk is less expensive, and, in the time it takes to create one or two meals, you can prepare food for the entire week, thereby saving hours every day that are normally used for dinner preparation. (Find a full guide to meal prep in Chapter 16.)

- **Friends and Family Together**—Anytime you work in a team, you hold each other accountable and create success together. Friends and family can help you achieve your goals. Sometimes this is not possible as not everyone in your household will want to be on the food plan you have adopted. You are responsible for your own health and wellness, and you cannot always rely on the whole household to join in; when you *can* get them to join in, you will all achieve more success together. If, however, you have to go it alone, find online partner sources such as social media associations and website groups.
- **Reduce Plate Size**—Literally reducing the size of the plates you use at home can help you keep your portions within reason. We Americans tend to fill our plates to the fullest, frowning upon empty space. Using a medium-sized salad plate instead of a large dinner plate forces you to keep your portions within reason. This helps you stay focused on eating the quantity and quality of foods that will help your inflammatory condition; over-eating does not help your overall health.
- **Prizes and Rewards**—A very positive self-motivational trick is to give yourself a reward when you hit your food goals. For example, did you reach your first week (or month, or year ...) on your specific food plan? Hooray! Reward yourself with something special such as a spa day, a movie at the theater, a bouquet of flowers, a new book, or join an interesting class or go on a fun outing. You deserve a reward for your dedication to your health; definitely take it.
- **Build a Commitment Contract**—When we promise ourselves we are going to stay on a health plan, then we fall off the program, this can be because we have not fully emotionally committed. Studies have demonstrated that people who made a verbal or written commitment in front of family or friends were far more likely to stick to their plan. Write up a contract and sign it. If you have a group of people participating in a food plan goal, then this encourages you all to stick with it.
- **Professional Assistance and Counseling**—In my personal experience, the best way to stay on an anti-inflammatory meal plan is to consult regularly with an expert who offers educated advice. A health-care professional, such as a doctor or nutritionist, is at the top of this list. My nutritionist has been counseling me for years on all things food. Her science-based guidance has been invaluable. Beyond a nutritionist, sometimes food concerns need to be escalated to the next level. If you have an eating disorder, are morbidly obese, or suffer from malnutrition or a food addiction, for instance, your food choices might be difficult to comprehend or control. A psychiatrist or professional counselor can help you discover the reasons you are struggling with food choices and, with the partnered help of your other health professionals, can help you find your way back to healthier eating.

REMEMBER ONE SIZE DOES NOT FIT ALL

YOU CAN DO THIS! I have personally gone through this food change process and know that building new habits can be uncomfortable and challenging. I believe in you and know you can build a wellness meal plan that works for you based on smart anti-inflammatory foods. Once you get past your first 30 to 60 days of eating smartly and with a lot more flavor, you will start to see a change in your habits and in your body.

It is important that for the first 30 to 60 days, you really stick to the plan. Cheating never benefited you in school and it does not benefit you now, because people can physically react to even a small amount of inflammatory food. Thinking "I'm just going to have dessert this one time!" can lead to a downward spiral of eating more and more foods that trigger inflammation as well as intense inflammatory pain. Then you have to start all over again. Sticking with an anti-inflammatory food plan for 30 to 60 days or more can help you keep those trigger foods out of your body so you can truly see the result of a low-inflammation experience.

Cheating with inflammatory foods is far more than "having a treat," it's consuming something that can set you back emotionally and physically with your chronic inflammatory condition.

As a result of being on my food plan for more than four years, my personal health changes have been incredible and noteworthy. Chronic inflammatory pain dramatically ruled my life, but in taking control of my body through an anti-inflammatory lifestyle, I was able to reduce my inflammatory pain and change my quality of life significantly.

Call a nutritionist or health professional, do some research, discover what flavors you love, and learn what works best for you so you can build your own anti-inflammatory plan. Each chapter of this cookbook will give you flavor-filled, nutritious, anti-inflammatory recipes you can fit into most any healthy and responsible diet or anti-inflammatory meal plan. In Chapter 16, the Meal Plan chapter, learn tips on how to prepare your meals in advance. This cookbook is more than a cookbook, it is your opportunity to find your health and wellness through smart, flavorful, anti-inflammatory food choices; if I can do it, then you can too.

YOU GOT THIS.
I BELIEVE IN YOU.

	Serving Size (g)	Glycemic Index	Calories (kcal)	Protein (g)	Lipid (g)	Carbohydrate (g)	Fiber (g)	Calcium (mg)
Apple	120	36.2	62	0.31	0.2	16.57	2.9	7
Apricot	120	45.5	58	1.68	0.47	13.34	2.4	16
Arugula	100	32	25	2.58	0.66	3.65	1.6	160
Artichoke	100	32	47	3.27	0.15	10.51	5.4	44
Asparagus	100	32	20	2.2	0.12	3.88	2.1	24
Avocado	100	50	160	2	14.66	8.53	6.7	12
Banana	120	53.3	107	1.31	0.4	27.41	3.1	6
Banana pepper	100	32	27	1.66	0.45	5.35	3.4	14
Basil	100	N/A	23	3.15	0.64	2.65	1.6	177
Beets	100	64	43	1.61	0.17	9.56	2.8	16
Bitter melon	100	32	17	1	0.17	3.7	2.8	19
Blackberries	100	N/A	43	1.39	0.49	9.61	5.3	29
Blueberries	100	40	57	0.74	0.33	14.49	2.4	6
Bok choy	100	N/A	13	1.5	0.2	2.18	1	105
Broccoli	100	32	34	2.82	0.37	6.64	2.6	47
Brussels sprouts	100	32	43	3.38	0.3	8.95	3.8	42
Cabbage, green	100	32	25	1.28	0.1	5.8	2.5	40
Cantaloupe	120	67.5	41	1.01	0.23	9.79	1.1	11
Carrots	80	16	33	0.74	0.19	7.66	2.2	26
Cassava	100	46	160	1.36	0.28	38.06	1.8	16
Cauliflower	100	32	25	1.92	0.28	4.97	2	22
Celeriac	100	N/A	42	1.5	0.3	9.2	1.8	43
Celery	100	32	16	0.69	0.17	2.97	1.6	40
Chard, Swiss	100	32	19	1.8	0.2	3.74	1.6	51
Chayote	100	N/A	19	0.82	0.13	4.51	1.7	17
Cherry	120	22	76	1.27	0.24	19.21	2.5	16
Corn	115	58	99	3.76	1.55	21.5	2.3	2
Cucumber	100	32	12	0.59	0.16	2.16	0.7	14
Dates	60	45.2	166	1.09	0.09	44.98	4	38
Eggplant	100	32	25	0.98	0.18	5.88	3	9
Endive	100	32	17	1.25	0.2	3.35	3.1	52
Fennel, bulb	100	N/A	31	1.24	0.2	7.3	3.1	49
Fennel seeds	50	N/A	172	7.9	7.43	26.14	19.9	598
Figs	100	61	74	0.75	0.3	19.18	2.9	35
Garlic	100	32	149	6.36	0.5	33.06	2.1	181
Grapefruit	120	25	38	0.76	0.12	9.7	1.3	14
Grapes	120	46	80	0.76	0.42	20.58	1.1	17
Honeydew melon	100	65	36	0.54	0.14	9.09	0.8	6

SOURCES: www.ndb.nal.usda.gov/ndb/search/list, www.nutritionsoftware.org/usda-nutrient-databases, www.glycemicindex.com/foodSearch.php, www.dietgrail.com/gid/, www.diabetes.org/food-and-fitness/food/what-can-i-eat/understanding-carbohydrates/glycemic-index-and-diabetes.html

Iron (mg)	Magnesium (mg)	Phosphorous (mg)	Potassium (mg)	Sodium (mg)	Zinc (mg)	Vitamin C (mg)	Vitamin A (IU)	Vitamin E (mg)	Vitamin K (µg)	Folate (µg)
0.14	6	13	128	1	0.05	5.5	65	0.22	2.6	4
0.47	12	28	311	1	0.24	12	2311	1.07	4	11
1.46	47	52	369	27	0.47	15	2373	0.43	108.6	97
1.28	60	90	370	94	0.49	11.7	13	0.19	14.8	68
2.14	14	52	202	2	0.54	5.6	756	1.13	41.6	52
0.55	29	52	485	7	0.64	10	146	2.07	21	81
0.31	32	26	430	1	0.18	10.4	77	0.12	0.6	24
0.46	17	32	256	13	0.25	82.7	340	0.69	9.5	29
3.17	64	56	295	4	0.81	18	5275	0.8	414.8	68
0.8	23	40	325	78	0.35	4.9	33	0.04	0.2	109
0.43	17	31	296	5	0.8	84	471	0	0	72
0.62	20	22	162	1	0.53	21	214	1.17	19.8	25
0.28	6	12	77	1	0.16	9.7	54	0.57	19.3	6
0.8	19	37	252	65	0.19	45	4468	0.09	45.5	66
0.73	21	66	316	33	0.41	89.2	623	0.78	101.6	63
1.4	23	69	389	25	0.42	85	754	0.88	177	61
0.47	12	26	170	18	0.18	36.6	98	0.15	76	43
0.25	14	18	320	19	0.22	44	4058	0.06	3	25
0.24	10	28	256	55	0.19	4.7	13365	0.53	10.6	15
0.27	21	27	271	14	0.34	20.6	13	0.19	1.9	27
0.42	15	44	299	30	0.27	48.2	0	0.08	15.5	57
0.7	20	115	300	100	0.33	8	0	0.36	41	8
0.2	11	24	260	80	0.13	3.1	449	0.27	29.3	36
1.8	81	46	379	213	0.36	30	6116	1.89	830	14
0.34	12	18	125	2	0.74	7.7	0	0.12	4.1	93
0.43	13	25	266	0	0.08	8.4	77	0.08	2.5	5
0.6	43	102	310	17	0.53	7.8	215	0.08	0.3	48
0.22	12	21	136	2	0.17	3.2	72	0.03	7.2	14
0.54	32	37	418	1	0.26	0	89	0	1.6	9
0.23	14	24	229	2	0.16	2.2	23	0.3	3.5	22
0.83	15	28	314	22	0.79	6.5	2167	0.44	231	142
0.73	17	50	414	52	0.2	12	963	0.58	62.8	27
9.27	192	244	847	44	1.85	10.5	68	0	0	0
0.37	17	14	232	1	0.15	2	142	0.11	4.7	6
1.7	25	153	401	17	1.16	31.2	9	0.08	1.7	3
0.11	10	10	167	0	0.08	41.3	1112	0.16	0	12
0.35	6	12	229	2	0.05	4.8	120	0.23	17.5	5
0.17	10	11	228	18	0.09	18	50	0.02	2.9	19

	Serving Size (g)	Glycemic Index	Calories (kcal)	Protein (g)	Lipid (g)	Carbohydrate (g)	Fiber (g)	Calcium (mg)
Jicama	100	32	38	0.72	0.09	8.82	4.9	12
Kale	100	32	49	4.28	0.93	8.75	3.6	150
Kiwi	120	52.5	73	1.37	0.62	17.59	3.6	41
Lettuce, romaine	100	32	17	1.23	0.3	3.29	2.1	33
Leeks	100	N/A	61	1.5	0.3	14.15	1.8	59
Lemon	100	N/A	29	1.1	0.3	9.32	2.8	26
Lime	100	N/A	30	0.7	0.2	10.54	2.8	33
Lychee	100	57	66	0.83	0.44	16.53	1.3	5
Mango	120	51	72	0.98	0.46	17.98	1.9	13
Mushrooms	100	32	22	3.09	0.34	3.26	1	3
Okra	100	32	33	1.93	0.19	7.45	3.2	82
Onions	100	32	40	1.1	0.1	9.34	1.7	23
Orange	120	42	56	1.13	0.14	14.1	2.9	48
Papaya	120	59	52	0.56	0.31	12.98	2	24
Parsley	100	32	36	2.97	0.79	6.33	3.3	138
Parsnips	80	52	57	1.06	0.24	13.61	2.9	30
Peach	120	42	47	1.09	0.3	11.45	1.8	7
Peas	100	48	81	5.42	0.4	14.45	5.7	25
Pears	100	38	57	0.36	0.14	15.23	3.1	9
Pineapple	120	66	54	0.66	0.16	14.18	0	16
Potatoes	150	85	116	3.07	0.14	26.23	3.2	18
Prunes	60	29	144	1.31	0.23	38.33	4.3	26
Pumpkin	100	75	26	1	0.1	6.5	0.5	21
Radishes	100	32	16	0.68	0.1	3.4	1.6	25
Raisins	60	65	179	1.84	0.28	47.51	2.2	30
Raspberries	100	N/A	52	1.2	0.65	11.94	6.5	25
Rhubarb	100	N/A	21	0.9	0.2	4.54	1.8	86
Rutabaga	150	72	56	1.62	0.24	12.93	3.4	64
Serrano pepper	100	32	32	1.74	0.44	6.7	3.7	11
Shallots	100	N/A	72	2.5	0.1	16.8	3.2	37
Spinach	100	32	23	2.86	0.39	3.63	2.2	99
Strawberry	100	N/A	32	0.67	0.3	7.68	2	16
Summer squash	100	32	17	1.21	0.32	3.11	1	16
Sweet pepper, red	100	32	31	0.99	0.3	6.03	2.1	7
Sweet potato	150	77	129	2.35	0.08	30.18	4.5	45
Tomatoes	100	38	18	0.88	0.2	3.89	1.2	10
Turnip	100	62	28	0.9	0.1	6.43	1.8	30
Watermelon	120	76	36	0.73	0.18	9.06	0.5	8
Zucchini	100	N/A	21	2.71	0.4	3.11	1.1	21

Iron (mg)	Magnesium (mg)	Phosphorous (mg)	Potassium (mg)	Sodium (mg)	Zinc (mg)	Vitamin C (mg)	Vitamin A (IU)	Vitamin E (mg)	Vitamin K (µg)	Folate (µg)
0.6	12	18	150	4	0.16	20.2	21	0.46	0.3	12
1.47	47	92	491	38	0.56	120	9990	1.54	704.8	141
0.37	20	41	374	4	0.17	111.2	104	1.75	48.4	30
0.97	14	30	247	8	0.23	4	8710	0.13	102.5	136
2.1	28	35	180	20	0.12	12	1667	0.92	47	64
0.6	8	16	138	2	0.06	53	22	0.15	0	11
0.6	6	18	102	2	0.11	29.1	50	0.22	0.6	8
0.31	10	31	171	1	0.07	71.5	0	0.07	0.4	14
0.19	12	17	202	1	0.11	43.7	1298	1.08	5	52
0.5	9	86	318	5	0.52	2.1	0	0.01	0	17
0.62	57	61	299	7	0.58	23	716	0.27	31.3	60
0.21	10	29	146	4	0.17	7.4	2	0.02	0.4	19
0.12	12	17	217	0	0.08	63.8	270	0.22	0	36
0.3	25	12	218	10	0.1	73.1	1140	0.36	3.1	44
6.2	50	58	554	56	1.07	133	8424	0.75	1640	152
0.46	23	55	294	8	0.21	10.4	0	0.8	0.8	46
0.3	11	24	228	0	0.2	7.9	391	0.88	3.1	5
1.47	33	108	244	5	1.24	40	765	0.13	24.8	65
0.18	7	12	116	1	0.1	4.3	25	0.12	4.4	7
0.3	14	11	150	1	0.1	20.3	62	0	0.8	13
1.22	34	86	638	9	0.45	29.5	3	0.01	3	22
0.56	25	41	439	1	0.26	0.4	469	0.26	35.7	2
0.8	12	44	340	1	0.32	9	8513	1.06	1.1	16
0.34	10	20	233	39	0.28	14.8	7	0	1.3	25
1.13	19	61	449	7	0.13	1.4	0	0.07	2.1	3
0.69	22	29	151	1	0.42	26.2	33	0.87	7.8	21
0.22	12	14	288	4	0.1	8	102	0.27	29.3	7
0.66	30	80	458	18	0.36	37.5	3	0.45	0.4	32
0.86	22	40	305	10	0.26	44.9	937	0.69	11.8	23
1.2	21	60	334	12	0.4	8	4	0.04	0.8	34
2.71	79	49	558	79	0.53	28.1	9377	2.03	482.9	194
0.41	13	24	153	1	0.14	58.8	12	0.29	2.2	24
0.37	18	38	261	8	0.32	17.9	200	0.12	4.3	24
0.43	12	26	211	4	0.25	127.7	3131	1.58	4.9	46
0.92	38	70	506	82	0.45	3.6	21280	0.39	2.7	16
0.27	11	24	237	5	0.17	13.7	833	0.54	7.9	15
0.3	11	27	191	67	0.27	21	0	0.03	0.1	15
0.29	12	13	134	1	0.12	9.7	683	0.06	0.1	4
0.79	33	93	459	3	0.83	34.1	490	0	0	20

A FLAVOR EXPLOSION

Herb and spice combinations that knock your socks off with taste.

Imagine a world where every bite is better than the one before. You can easily do this with herbs, spices, and smart cooking techniques. When we discover the best ways to add flavor to a healthful anti-inflammatory meal, it transforms and elevates the food from simply being good for us to being the wonderful moment we live for every day. Food is more than "the cure"—food is and can be joyous when it is infused with over-the-top delicious tastes.

Increasing flavor utilizing an anti-inflammatory or elimination diet is possible and wonderfully easy by stacking the flavors. One of the best ways to increase flavor is to add herbs and spices during the cooking process, stacking them one on top of the other. Making your own spice blends can bring its own reward in a fresher level of tastiness, enhancing your food with enriched color, scent, and taste. Stacking food with taste is stacking healthful food in your favor!

CHAPTER ONE

STACKED IN YOUR FLAVOR

--- *in this chapter* ---

You can have a flavor explosion every time you take a bite when you learn the secret of stacking flavors, which really means to layer and combine herbs, spices, citrus, oils, and foods to increase deliciousness at every opportunity.

When we are given a "food prescription" to treat an inflammatory condition like diabetes or heart disease, we often look at the list of dairy-free, grain-free, sugar-free items we can eat such as steamed broccoli or grilled chicken and feel frustrated at the blandness of the prescribed foods. Yet these foods are full of nutrition and can have a lot of over-the-top flavor if we simply prepare them properly and with a bit of flare.

Seasoning mix flavors are "stacked," assembling each ingredient into a more complex and enticing flavor profile that helps enhance food and make it taste better.

SEASONING MIXES

HOW TO STACK AND SWAP FLAVORS

Stacking and swapping flavors means combining herbs and spices into your own spice blends and layering them throughout your recipes while cooking. For example, for every pound of vegetables in a dish, add one to two tablespoons of an herb or spice. If you like more, ADD MORE! If you prefer less, ADD LESS! This is your opportunity to make your food match your personal taste.

Expand your flavor palate and layer more flavors by creating your own seasoning mixes that combine your favorite herbs and spices into a delicious foundation for the dish you are preparing.

Let's say you love riced cauliflower flavored with Italian Seasoning Mix as much as I do, but you are craving variety and want to kick it up a notch. Simply replace your Italian seasoning blend with the same quantity of Fajita Spice Seasoning Mix or Curry Spice Seasoning Mix for an explosion of flavor. Swapping flavors can add an immense level of variety to the same old dishes you've been preparing for years, and they can encourage you and your family to consume more vegetables and other healthful foods.

Chapter 2 contains a number of spice-blend recipes.

Making your own seasoning combinations is super easy. You will need airtight containers to store the seasonings, a funnel, and individual dried spices, herbs, or citrus zest.

This delicious recipe for Jamaican Jerk Seasoning is easy to make and full of Caribbean flavor.

Mixing it is easy: Measure all the spices into a small bowl or cup, then funnel into an airtight container (see the photograph above). Shake well to mix the ingredients, and store in a cool, dry place in order to preserve all those yummy flavors.

If herbs and spices are exposed to air, sunlight, or hot temperatures, they are likely to lose potency more quickly. Generally speaking, whole spices will stay fresh for nearly four years, while ground or crushed spices will stay fresh for three years. Dried leafy herbs can last between one to three years, but are best under a year. Citrus zest can be refrigerated when freshly zested—if covered tightly—for a week or so, but zest also can be dried and used for up to three years. If the flavor has ebbed due to aging, simply add more of the herbs and spices to your dishes to increase the flavor.

BAKED CHICKEN FLAVOR SWAP

WITH JAMAICAN JERK SEASONING MIX

 3 1/2 TO 5 1/2 HOURS

 YIELDS 1/4 CUP SEASONING

 YIELDS 4 SERVINGS

Jamaican Jerk Seasoning Mix

INGREDIENTS

- 2 tablespoons onion powder
- 1 tablespoon salt
- 1 tablespoon thyme
- 1 teaspoon ground allspice
- 1 1/2 teaspoons cinnamon
- 1/2 teaspoon cayenne powder
- 1/2 teaspoon minced ginger

Baked Chicken Flavor Swap

INGREDIENTS

- 1 pound chicken pieces with skin removed
- 1 tablespoon vegetable or olive oil
- 2 tablespoons Jamaican Jerk Seasoning Mix (or flavor swap another seasoning mix)

INSTRUCTIONS

1. Combine all the seasonings, mixing well (or grinding with a mortar and pestle).
2. Place in an airtight jar.
3. Store in a cool, dry location.

～～～～～～～～

1. Rub chicken pieces with the seasoning mix (this time Jamaican Jerk Seasoning, next time with another favorite), cover and refrigerate for 2 to 4 hours.
2. Heat oven to 350 F.
3. Drizzle the oil into a 9-by-13-inch baking dish.
4. Place the marinated chicken pieces skin-side up in the baking dish.
5. Bake for 80 minutes (checking regularly) until chicken registers 165 F on a meat thermometer and the meat is no longer pink near the bone.

GENERAL ROASTING TIME FOR
CUT VEGETABLES

UP TO 70 MINUTES

VARIES

Taste buds are powerful receptors and have the ability to distinguish five flavors: sweet, salty, sour, bitter, and savory (also known as "umami"). Finding ways to help our taste buds distinguish these flavors in higher concentrations can enable us to have a happier, and more flavorful, dining experience.

1. **Roast Vegetables & Garlic**—Roasting helps caramelize and release flavors so vegetables taste more intense when they hit your palate. Roast vegetables at 425 degrees in order to fully release their flavors (see the chart at left). Roasted garlic turns into a spreadable delight as smooth as butter.

2. **Sear, Brown, or Caramelize Meats & Fish**—Meat and fish require varying temperatures to sear, brown, or caramelize. These terms describe the reaction when proteins and sugars come into contact with dry heat through grilling, pan frying, or roasting. The result is a richer, more penetrating flavor with cooking times varying depending on the weight and consistency of the food and the oils used.

3. **Add Herbs, Spices, & Citrus**—When you combine fresh herbs and spices with rather ordinary vegetables and meat, you transform a dish into something remarkably flavorful. Citrus zest and juice add gusto and acidic flavor to salads, vegetables, and meat.

TIMES PER VEGGIE

Cut into 1-inch pieces and roast at 425 F.

(Cooking time will vary depending on personal preference.)

- **Cruciferous Vegetables**
  15 to 30 minutes
- **General Vegetables**
  10 to 25 minutes
- **Onions & Garlic**
  30 to 45 minutes
- **Root Vegetables**
  45 minutes
- **Summer Squash & Tomatoes**
  15 to 20 minutes
- **Winter Squash**
  20 to 70 minutes

ROASTED VEGETABLES
FLAVOR SWAP

UP TO 60 MINUTES

YIELDS 4 SERVINGS

Throughout my childhood, we had a sit-down Sunday dinner, a chance for our crazy family to get together and eat a feast of magnificent portions, which my grandmother prepared. While I loved the family time, the reality was that the food was full of all the things it would be better to not include—lots of deep-fried foods smothered in gravy and desserts filled with layers of sugar, and we ate until we were all stuffed. Over-eating and eating unhealthy food are ways to trigger inflammation.

My introduction to roasting vegetables was when my grandmother roasted broccoli, then smothered the vegetable with cheese, crackers, and butter. This was my normal food growing up, so breaking the habit of consuming all those fat-filled, inflammatory-triggering recipes and rebuilding my vision for how to roast vegetables became a major challenge in building my anti-inflammatory meal plan.

What I discovered is that roasting releases the sugars in the vegetables and enables caramelization, increasing the flavor of the dish tremendously. You do not need all the gravy, cheese, and oil to make a vegetable taste memorable. Roasted vegetables have flavor that is wonderful, particularly when you add your favorite herbs and spices.

INGREDIENTS

- 1 pound vegetables (your choice), peeled and cut into 1-inch pieces
- 1 tablespoon extra-virgin olive oil
- 1 teaspoon salt
- Pepper, to taste
- 1 tablespoon chopped herbs or 1 tablespoon flavor swap seasoning mix (pick your favorite; I like Italian Seasoning, Page 75)

INSTRUCTIONS

1. Heat oven to 425 F.
2. Place vegetables in bowl, adding olive oil, salt, pepper, and herbs (more than 1 tablespoon if you want more flavor). Toss until vegetables are evenly coated with herbs.
3. Spread vegetables in a single layer on a baking sheet or baking dish. Do not crowd.
4. Roast vegetables. Check every 15 minutes until they are tender and can be pierced with a fork. Crispy or slightly blackened bits are desirable. Serve immediately.

Here's the thing; cauliflower rice is not actually rice, the grain we all use with stir-fry dishes. Cauliflower rice, however, is mind blowing in the sense that it can be transformed into something surprising. When the trend to use cauliflower rice as a side dish first came about, I felt rather distrustful of the stuff. It comes from a cruciferous vegetable that has a lot of crunch, so how can it be similar to rice? What I discovered is that raw cauliflower rice is, in fact, absolutely genius in a leafy green salad or a salad made of quinoa because the crunch-factor is high and it truly adds some panache to a plain salad.

Cooking raw cauliflower rice transforms it into a tender and chewy white substance that has a similar consistency to rice. I use it regularly as a newly imagined rice beneath grilled salmon or as a prime ingredient in a curry vegetable stir-fry.

If you prepare the riced cauliflower recipe on the next page and leave it "plain" with only a little olive oil and salt instead of a seasoning mix, it reminds me of couscous. Riced cauliflower is absolutely perfect as a filler for burritos and other hot sandwiches, can be made into a bread or pizza crust, and even works well as a rice substitute in sushi.

BASIC RICED CAULIFLOWER

UP TO 30 MINUTES

YIELDS 4 SERVINGS

INGREDIENTS

- 1 head raw cauliflower (fresh out of the garden is best)
- Raw vegetables such as peas, carrots, and onions (optional)
- 1 tablespoon olive or coconut oil
- 1 to 2 tablespoons seasoning mix or individual herbs or spices

INSTRUCTIONS

1. Wash and thoroughly dry cauliflower.
2. Using a food processor or a box grater, chop or grate the cauliflower and vegetables into small, rice-sized pieces.
3. Place in a clean tea towel and squeeze tightly to remove any excess moisture.
4. Use raw in salads or sauté the cauliflower rice in a large skillet over medium heat in 1 tablespoon olive oil.
5. Add individual herbs or spices or swap in any flavor of seasoning mix (or go without seasoning for a "plain" cauliflower flavor).
6. When cooking, cover with a lid so the cauliflower steams and becomes slightly tender, cooking for a total of 5 to 8 minutes (longer if desired).
7. Leftovers keep in the refrigerator for up to 5 days. Store uncooked cauliflower rice in freezer for up to 6 weeks.

TO SALT OR NOT TO SALT
THAT IS THE QUESTION

An argument has been raging since the early 1900s on the question of salt's ability to raise blood pressure. Recent studies have proven a low-salt diet releases certain enzymes and hormones that decrease blood pressure, somewhat contradicting the more commonly known theory from other studies that salt causes higher blood pressure. However, continuing to consume salt in moderation is a smart goal. *The Dietary Guidelines for Americans* recommends 2,300 milligrams of sodium per day, yet the average American consumes about 3,400 milligrams. These numbers are remarkably reduced when you make the choice to eat more fresh foods and eliminate packaged and ultra-processed foods.

I like to lightly grind both salt and pepper over my food while I'm cooking. Pepper is greatly enhanced by grinding. While salt flavor is not enhanced as much, it allows me to control the size of the grain. Pre-ground flavored salts are also tasty choices. Different types of flavored salts are essentially known as seasoning salts and are similar to the seasoning mixes in this cookbook—they are created from blending various essences with salt and are meant to enhance the flavor of food.

A FEW TYPES OF SALT

- **Black Lava Salt**—Typically made in Hawaii, this salt is infused with activated charcoal.
- **Celery Salt**—A mixture of celery seeds and sea salt.
- **Himalayan Salt**—Used for therapeutic and cosmetic benefits as well as culinary, this salt, found in Pakistan, has various minerals that cause the pink shade.
- **Large Flake Salt**—This salt is large, flaky, and crystalline in shape and offers a heavier crunch.
- **Red Alaea Salt**—Mixed with purified red alaea clay found in Hawaii.
- **Sea Salt**—White with various consistencies.
- **Seasoning Salt**—Mix of any variety of herbs or spices such as garlic or onion powder, oregano, cumin, rosemary, basil, paprika, ground red pepper, and different types of peppercorns. Available in a variety of combinations in grocery stores, or make your own.
- **Smoked Sea Salt**—Smoked with various types of woods and methods, this salt adds a rich aroma and a smoky flavor.
- **Table Salt**—Typically mined and processed to eliminate minerals, often with added iodine or other chemical additives.

CHAPTER TWO

NORTH AMERICAN
STYLE FLAVORS

——————— *in this chapter* ———————

North American flavors are full of delicious herbs and spice combinations mixed with meats, salads, and side dishes. In this chapter, you will find basil, bay leaf, chiles, cilantro, cumin, dill, and garlic, among others. They are important to Cajun, chili, fajita, ranch, and taco seasoning blends. Like North America, the flavors are a melting pot of creative tastes: a mix of Africa, Mexico, the Mediterranean, and Old World Europe—all bringing their unique enthusiasm to every flavorful bite. Transform the lowly vegetable into something magnificent with seasonings and a bit of oil.

Infusing is an amazing way to stack enticing flavors into oils. These oils can then be used in salads, sauces, marinades, or to sauté meat and vegetables, and they can truly add some delicious energy to your recipes. However, there is an important concern to consider when utilizing infused oils; they can be extremely dangerous if not prepared properly. The risk is the formation of a deadly microorganism, *Clostridium botulinum* (*C. bot*), which can cause botulism. The result is highly unsafe for humans as it is highly debilitating and can cause death.

The danger is primarily in adding fresh fruit, vegetables, and herbs to the oils. These fresh low-acid foods can be contaminated with *C. bot* spores. They might also contain water, which enables the *C. bot* bacteria to thrive and grow. Industrial and commercial producers acidify the oil product with bacteria inhibitors during production in order to prevent the microorganism's growth so the oils do not spoil and can be stored at room temperature. It is not recommended to acidify the oils at home because of safety concerns, so it is better to incorporate specific foods, herbs, or flavorings that will prevent *C. bot* growth. This will allow you to create safe and healthy oils for use in your home kitchen.

Infusing with heat by using a slow cooker speeds the process up to one day or less, where traditional infusing takes four to six weeks. All oils can go rancid whenever stored for more than three months. Although rancid vegetable oil does not smell, look, or taste different from regular oil, it has been linked to early aging and cancer in numerous studies. Storing all oils in a cool, dry, dark place helps prevent rancidity and enables your infused flavors to shine. Store properly and discard after three months.

HOW TO INFUSE OILS WITH A
SLOW COOKER

INGREDIENTS TO SAFELY INFUSE IN OILS

- Dried citrus rind
- Dried garlic; fresh garlic is to be avoided completely
- Dried herbs: Whole dried stems are particularly beautiful in a jar
- Dried peppers: All peppers taste different and can be hot, mild, or smoky
- Dried produce such as sun-dried tomatoes
- Seeds such as caraway, cumin, fennel, or mustard seed
- Whole black peppercorns

INSTRUCTIONS

1. When infusing oils, use a glass container with a lid that seals. Sanitize the glass by boiling in water for 30 to 60 seconds, then remove and let dry completely. Do this for all the containers to be used for production and storage.
2. Choose a quality cold-pressed oil such as avocado oil for your carrier oil.
3. Add the infusing ingredient in the bottom of a slow cooker and slowly add the oil.
4. Heat the slow cooker on high until the oil smells delicious or has changed color slightly, letting you know the infusion has worked. This usually takes several hours, but some flavorings will take more than eight hours. Turn off the slow cooker and let the oil cool completely.
5. To make the bottles more attractive, place additional flavor ingredients in a clean and dry bottle or container, filling half full, if desired.
6. Strain cooled oil through a fine sieve, and pour oil into the bottle.
7. Cap the container and store in a cool, dry place for up to three months.

My favorite of all infusion oils is dried red chile peppers and garlic. So insanely delicious! While red chile oil is commonly used in Italian and Moroccan dishes, it is also a fantastic kick in the pants for meat marinades and Mexican cooking. Make it using the slower technique of infusing without a slow cooker for less fuss and muss in the kitchen. Be careful when making this to keep the essence of the oil from getting in your eyes. Wear gloves or wash your hands immediately after handling chiles and oil.

KICK-IN-THE-PANTS
RED CHILE OIL

UP TO 6 WEEKS

VARIES DEPENDING ON AMOUNT OF OIL

INGREDIENTS

- Olive oil
- 1/4 cup whole dried chile peppers
- 2 tablespoons minced dried garlic
- 3 tablespoons crushed dried red pepper flakes

INSTRUCTIONS

1. Follow directions below for infusing oils WITHOUT a slow cooker.
2. Place the ingredients in each Mason jar.
3. Infuse over several weeks, then strain completely, retaining the whole dried chile peppers.
4. Place remaining whole chile peppers in the bottle, then fill with flavored oil.

HOW TO INFUSE OILS WITHOUT A SLOW COOKER

1. To infuse oils, use a glass container with a lid that seals. Sanitize the glass by boiling in water for 30 to 60 seconds, then remove and let dry completely. Do this for all the containers to be used for production and storage.
2. Choose a quality cold-pressed oil such as olive oil or avocado oil for your carrier oil.
3. Place flavor ingredients in a clean and dry container such as a Mason jar, filling half to two-thirds full.
4. Pour unheated carrier oil into the bottle.
5. Cap the container and store in a cool, dry place for four to six weeks, allowing the flavors to marry.
6. After four to six weeks, strain the oil through a fine sieve and place in sanitized bottles, capping tightly.

CAJUN SEASONING

Cajun food is near and dear to my heart. I once met a lovely couple from southern Louisiana, Dickie and Renee, who declared themselves Cajun through and through. They owned a sugar cane plantation and crawfish farm south of the I-10 highway right smack in the middle of Louisiana Cajun Country. They invited me to a hole-in-the-wall crab shack so I could try Cajun-style soft-shell crabs, frog legs, étouffée, and crawfish boulettes. The food was delicious and the people were quite wonderful with their Cajun accents and giving hearts. I learned the primary flavor palate for Cajun cuisine on that trip and use it often to add a flavorful angle to my recipes. The trick is that the food is filled with flavor and not spiciness like we often think. Whenever I make a Cajun dish, I think of sultry-hot summer picnics and laughter.

WAYS TO ADD CAJUN FLAVOR TO YOUR DISHES

1. **Cajun Mirepoix**—The French influence is strong in Cajun Country and flavors are often based on a version of the French mirepoix, which includes celery, onion, and green bell pepper. This is known as "the holy trinity of Cajun cuisine."

2. **Add Garlic**—Garlic is a primary ingredient in most dishes.

3. **Add More Flavor**—Use green onions, parsley, paprika, thyme, filé (which is ground sassafras leaves), bay leaf, and salt to up the flavor quotient.

4. **Add Sausage**—Andouille and tasso sausage are Cajun-based delicacies and are great when added to stews and other dishes. Be cautious of boudin sausage as it usually has rice in it. Find fresh, preservative-free sausages with fewer chemicals, whenever possible.

5. **Add Cauliflower Rice**—Rice is served often at the Cajun table; you can easily substitute with riced cauliflower if you are avoiding grains.

6. **Seasoning Mix**—Mix up the Cajun Country seasoning blend on the next page and use it often as a seasoning flavor swap in your recipes.

CAJUN COUNTRY
SPICE SEASONING MIX

10 MINUTES

YIELDS 3/4 CUP

INGREDIENTS

- 2 tablespoons paprika
- 1 1/2 tablespoons salt
- 1 tablespoon garlic powder
- 2 tablespoons onion powder
- 1 tablespoon cayenne pepper
- 2 tablespoons crushed oregano leaf
- 1 tablespoon crushed thyme leaf
- 1 1/2 teaspoons black pepper

INSTRUCTIONS

1. Combine all the seasonings, mixing well (or grinding with a mortar and pestle).
2. Place in an airtight jar.
3. Store in a cool, dry location.

CHILI SPICE
SEASONING MIX

10 MINUTES

YIELDS 1/4 CUP

Chili seasoning is the staple ingredient in any great chili soup, which is an American favorite. Historians say that chili con carne, a mixture of chile peppers, venison, onions, and tomatoes first came about in the early 1700s, but myths abound. We know that Lady Bird Johnson, when she was first lady, mailed out thousands of copies of President Lyndon B. Johnson's favorite chili recipe as so many people requested it. The below bean chili recipe came from my grandmother and is filled with country love.

INGREDIENTS

- 2 tablespoons chili powder
- 1 1/2 teaspoons garlic powder
- 1 tablespoon oregano
- 2 teaspoons onion powder
- 1 1/2 teaspoons paprika
- 1 1/2 teaspoons cumin
- 3/4 teaspoon thyme

INSTRUCTIONS

1. Combine all the seasonings, mixing well (or grinding with a mortar and pestle).
2. Place in an airtight jar.
3. Store in a cool, dry location.

THICK & RICH
BEAN CHILI

UP TO 7 HOURS

YIELDS 12+ SERVINGS

INGREDIENTS

- 1 pound ground poultry, red meat, or other protein, cooked
- 1 onion, finely chopped
- 1 green bell pepper, finely chopped
- 1 can (15 ounces) black beans, drained and rinsed
- 1 can (15 ounces) kidney beans, drained and rinsed
- 1 can (28 ounces) crushed tomatoes
- 1 can (14 1/2 ounces) diced tomatoes
- 2 tablespoons Chili Spice Seasoning Mix (Page 46)
- Cayenne pepper, to taste
- Salt and pepper, to taste
- Vegetable or chicken broth to reach desired soup consistency

INSTRUCTIONS

1. Place all ingredients in a slow cooker; stir to combine.
2. Cook on high 4 to 6 hours, adding more liquid if needed.

Ranch dressing seasoning, when combined with buttermilk, is the magical sauce Americans put on everything from salads to burgers to pizza. Bottled ranch dressing is currently the No. 1 dressing shipped around the United States, but bottled dressings can be filled with dairy and other unwanted ingredients. Love ranch dressing, but need a more healthful, lower-chemical solution? This mix is the answer.

RANCH DRESSING
SEASONING MIX

10 MINUTES

YIELDS 1/2 CUP

INGREDIENTS

- 2 tablespoons dried parsley leaf
- 1 1/2 tablespoons dill
- 1 1/2 tablespoons garlic powder
- 1 1/2 tablespoons onion powder
- 1/2 teaspoon basil leaf
- 1/2 teaspoon ground black pepper

INSTRUCTIONS

1. Combine all the seasonings, mixing well (or grinding with a mortar and pestle).
2. Place in an airtight jar.
3. Store in a cool, dry location.

IDEAS FOR USING MIX

1. **Poultry Amazingness**—Oil chicken pieces, then roll in Ranch Dressing Seasoning Mix.
2. **Marinade**—Combine with oil and a few tablespoons of citrus juice.
3. **Bread Topping**—Combine with oil and brush on any grain-full or grain-free cracker, bread, or crust.
4. **Vegetables**—Excellent sprinkled over vegetables before baking.
5. **Buttermilk-Style Dressing**—Use half the Ranch Dressing Seasoning Mix recipe combined with 1 cup soy-free mayonnaise, 1 tablespoon cider vinegar, 1 tablespoon dairy-free milk, and 1 heaping teaspoon fresh chopped chives. Use an immersion blender or place in a Mason jar and shake, shake, shake.

Mexican ranch workers living along the Rio Grande in Texas are said to have invented fajitas, cooking the meat and vegetables on camp grills. This taste sensation is full of flavor and has exuberantly spread across the culinary world.

When I was growing up in Indiana, there were no traditional Mexican restaurants near our farm and our family did not know of this delightful cuisine. This tasty Fajita Spice Seasoning Mix is a way to dip your toe into Tex-Mex cuisine much like I did while discovering my passion for Mexican food. You can go traditional and mix the fajita seasoning in your skirt steak fajitas, but I like to make fajitas with chicken, shrimp, and fish for a more healthful twist.

QUICK FAJITAS
WITH FAJITA SPICE SEASONING MIX

 10 MINUTES    YIELDS 1/4 CUP   30 MINUTES   YIELDS 4 SERVINGS

Fajita Spice Seasoning Mix

INGREDIENTS

- 1 tablespoon chili powder
- 1 tablespoon salt
- 1 tablespoon paprika
- 1 1/2 teaspoons onion powder
- 1 1/2 teaspoons garlic powder
- 1 1/2 teaspoons cumin powder
- 1/4 teaspoon cayenne powder

Quick Fajitas

INGREDIENTS

- 1/2 cup oil
- 1/4 cup lime juice (about 3 medium limes)
- 1 to 2 tablespoons Fajita Spice Seasoning Mix
- 1 pound chicken or other meat or protein, sliced thin
- 3 bell peppers, sliced thin
- 1 large onion, sliced thin
- Salt and pepper, to taste
- Several tortillas

INSTRUCTIONS

1. Combine all the seasonings, mixing well (or grinding with a mortar and pestle).
2. Place in an airtight jar.
3. Store in a cool, dry location.

~~~~~~~~~~~~~~~~~~~~~~~~~~~~~

1. In a big bowl, whisk together the first three ingredients.
2. Season meat and vegetables with salt and pepper, then toss in the bowl and evenly coat with oil mixture. Marinate for 5 to 10 minutes.
3. Place mixture in a hot cast-iron skillet, stirring quickly until vegetables are soft and meat is cooked through. Serve with warm tortillas (your choice of type or try one of my favorite no-grain tortilla recipes, Grain-Free Ranch Hand Tortillas, on Page 93).

CHAPTER THREE

ASIAN
STYLE FLAVORS

in this chapter

The Asian territory hosts close to 60 percent of the world's population, stretching from Russia to Japan to Indonesia to India to Saudi Arabia, with dozens of countries in between. Asian flavor profiles are known as some of the spiciest and widely varied in the world. Depending on what type of Asian-inspired food you are preparing, black pepper, chiles, coconut, ginger, wasabi, citrus, and garlic are strong influences. Don't like those flavors? No problem! Try fresh herbs like chives, coriander, lemongrass, mint, parsley, or Thai basil chopped into your basic salad dressings or stir-fried with your favorite proteins. Delve into Asian five-spice, cardamom, curry, and coconut Thai seasonings. Asian-inspired flavors can be wildly exciting and a fabulous way to change up your daily recipe routine.

THE MASHAMARATOR
HOW TO USE A MORTAR AND PESTLE

When I first heard of using a mortar and pestle, I thought it was a technique from ancient times. Seriously. Ancient. I opposed using the tool thinking the mess and cleanup was not worth the trouble. Besides that, it is bulky and a bit heavy, and where the heck am I going to put one of these things anyway? Well ... hold on to your hats, people, because I was wrong. I guarantee you that once you try using a mortar and pestle, you will be a better cook for it and also addicted forever to The Mashamarator.

FOOD PROCESSOR VS. MORTAR AND PESTLE

Yes, you could use a food processor to do some of the same things you do with a mortar and pestle, but you will get two completely different results. Simply put, a food processor cuts herbs, while a mortar and pestle crushes herbs. That process of pulverizing a plant, spice, or other ingredient forces the expulsion of essential oils, releases hidden flavors and aromas, and mashes ingredients into a marriage of over-the-top taste.

If you use a food processor to mince garlic and mince ginger to create an incorporated paste, you will be sorely disappointed. If you use a mortar and pestle to crush the smithereens out of garlic and ginger, swirling the pestle in circles as you smash, you will end up with a ginger-garlic paste explosion of deliciousness.

GETTING STARTED

1. Clean and season a new mortar and pestle, much like you would a cast-iron skillet (never use soap). Begin by washing the mortar and pestle without detergent in warm water using a stiff brush. Let it dry.
2. Grind a handful of uncooked rice until pulverized into powder. You will see gray granite dust mixed in. Shake out the powder and dust. Continue to add rice and swirl in rotating motions and pounding until the rice powder looks completely white, indicating that any loose granite has been removed. Shake out the dust.
3. Add a large bulb of garlic, peeled, and a handful of salt to the mortar. Pulverize the ingredients to a paste, spread paste over the mortar, and let it set for 18 to 24 hours. Rinse out with water.

HOW TO USE WITH SPICES AND OTHER INGREDIENTS

1. Place your ingredients in a dry mortar in a single layer. If you're using spices or seeds, start lightly thumping and pounding with your pestle, gently turning the mortar as you begin to crack the ingredients and release the oils.
2. Once you have cracked open the layer of ingredients, it is time to grind. Place the pestle in the center of the mortar on top of the cracked items and without lifting it, begin stirring and using a downward pressure. Grind it round and round; the more you grind, the finer the ingredients will get.
3. Order to add ingredients in mortar and pestle:
   a. Dry ingredients first
   b. Moist ingredients next
   c. Oily ingredients next
   d. Liquid ingredients last

CURRY SPICE
SEASONING MIX

10 MINUTES

YIELDS 3/4 CUP

Curry powder was originally a creation of the British and was meant to resemble the spice mixes from Northern India. However, many traditional Indian cooks say they never use curry powder; they use their own spice combinations to create more customized "curry." Indeed, that is the reason to make your own curry seasoning mix as well. Perhaps you like more turmeric with your curry for its anti-inflammatory properties, or you prefer a hotter curry powder with more red pepper flakes, or maybe you like a sweeter curry powder with cinnamon as a more pronounced ingredient.

I like the flavor of a yellow curry powder, heavy with turmeric. Instead of using it for rich Indian dishes filled with cream, I am more likely to use my curry as an all-purpose seasoning. Make a standard soup, stew, sauce, marinade, meat or vegetable dish, and add 1 to 2 tablespoons of curry. My favorite thing is to cut a hard-boiled egg in half, dollop a bit of non-soy mayonnaise on top, then sprinkle generously with Curry Spice Seasoning Mix and serve on top of lettuce. What a yummy lunch treat—like a bite of pure fun in your mouth and great in a lettuce wrap.

Whatever your preference, start with Curry Spice Seasoning Mix as a foundation, experiment, and see where adventurous flavors take you.

INGREDIENTS

- 2 tablespoons paprika
- 1 tablespoon cumin
- 3/4 teaspoon fennel powder
- 1 1/2 teaspoons fenugreek powder
- 1 1/2 teaspoons mustard powder
- 1 teaspoon ground red pepper flakes
- 2 teaspoons coriander powder
- 1 tablespoon ground turmeric
- 1 teaspoon ground cardamom
- 1/4 teaspoon cinnamon
- 1/8 teaspoon ground cloves

INSTRUCTIONS

1. Combine all the seasonings, mixing well (or grinding with a mortar and pestle).
2. Place in an airtight jar.
3. Store in a cool, dry location.

CRAZY DELICIOUS
CHICKEN CURRY STIR-FRY
FOR ONE

15 TO 20 MINUTES

YIELDS 1 SERVINGS

Have a busy life? Yep, I'm with you. If I'm tasked with a busy week, rotisserie chicken is my handy-helper. I use every inch of the meat off a rotisserie chicken and then boil the chicken bones for broth for the next week's meal-prepped dishes. If you aren't a fan of rotisserie chicken from the shops, you can bake whole chickens in advance, then—for both of them—tear off the meat and freeze in convenient portions for food prep.

When I'm at home alone and need a fast lunch or dinner, the Crazy Delicious Chicken Curry Stir-Fry for One is the thing I turn to; it's healthful and easy to throw together. Stir-frying the vegetables only takes a few minutes, tearing apart the chicken and adding the flavorings takes another few minutes. All in all, this flavorful dish takes very little time to prepare, and it tastes like a feast for the gods. It's also a smart meal prep choice.

INGREDIENTS

- 1 tablespoon olive oil
- 2 cups mixed vegetables of your choice
- 1/2 cup rotisserie or roasted chicken, torn into small pieces
- 1 tablespoon minced garlic
- 1 tablespoon Curry Spice Seasoning Mix (or more) (Page 55)
- 1/2 cup coconut milk or broth
- 1/2 teaspoon cayenne pepper (optional, if you like it hot)
- Salt and pepper, to taste

INSTRUCTIONS

1. Heat oil in a cast-iron skillet or wok to medium-high heat.
2. Toss in vegetables and chicken; stir-fry until lightly golden.
3. Add in garlic and seasoning mix. Stir-fry quickly until cooked.
4. Pour in coconut milk, and heat through. Salt and pepper to taste.
5. Serve hot.

DRIED GINGER
INFUSED OIL

UP TO 6 WEEKS

YIELD VARIES DEPENDING
ON AMOUNT OF OIL

Ginger is spicy when eaten in large quantities. Just a touch of ginger-infused oil is a lovely topper on chicken and other meats, though it is best mixed with salad dressings and marinades.

INGREDIENTS

- Oil to fill Mason jars
- 1/2 cup whole dry ginger, sliced thin
- 2 tablespoons minced dried garlic
- 1 tablespoon black or white peppercorns

INSTRUCTIONS

1. Follow directions on Page 43 for infusing oils WITHOUT a slow cooker.
2. Place the above ingredients in each Mason jar.
3. Infuse over 4 to 6 weeks, then strain completely. Fill bottles with flavored oil.

FRESH GINGER
INFUSED OIL

10 MINUTES

YIELDS 1/2 CUP

Another way to make an infused oil is to make it fresh, just before you put it on a salad or use it as a flavor-filled oil for a stir-fry. This ginger oil is almost as much ginger and garlic as it is oil—use wherever it calls for oil and be fabulously surprised by the added flavor.

INGREDIENTS

- 5 tablespoons oil
- 2 tablespoons peeled and grated fresh ginger
- 2 tablespoons peeled and grated or crushed fresh garlic

INSTRUCTIONS

1. Pour all ingredients into a Mason jar and store in the refrigerator for up to two weeks.

NO SOY & LOVIN' IT
TASTY THAI VINAIGRETTE DRESSING

10 MINUTES

YIELDS 3/4 CUP

Asian salad dressings are light, spicy, and delicious. I love them, but have been struggling for years to find a Thai-inspired dressing at a restaurant without soy and rice vinegar. Below is my solution for a super tasty Thai salad dressing that is free of soy, yet will impress your guests. They definitely won't miss the soy.

This dressing is yummy over stronger greens like kale and shredded cabbage, and works doubly well as a chicken or fish marinade. To make an Asian lettuce wrap, tear up a rotisserie chicken, chop some cabbage, carrots, or onions, wrap in lettuce leaves, then drizzle this dressing over it all. Yum!

INGREDIENTS

- 4 tablespoons avocado or olive oil
- 3 tablespoons white vinegar (or rice vinegar, if you are able to consume grains)
- 1 1/2 tablespoons sesame oil
- 1 tablespoon sunflower seed butter or almond butter (optional)
- 2 tablespoons citrus juice
- 2 tablespoons coconut aminos (optional; this tastes like soy sauce, and I prefer leaving it out of the recipe)
- 1 tablespoon Coconut Thai Spice Seasoning Mix (Page 65)
- 2 teaspoons grated fresh ginger
- 1 fresh garlic clove, minced
- Salt and pepper to taste

INSTRUCTIONS

1. Blend ingredients together in food processor or use a mortar and pestle.
2. Serve drizzled over salad or use as a marinade. Works great on salads made from stronger flavored greens.
3. Serve immediately; the dressing will store for a few days if refrigerated.

CHINESE 5-SPICE
SEASONING MIX

10 MINUTES

YIELDS 1/4 CUP

Another seasoning that can truly give a distinctive touch to your food is Five-Spice Powder, which originated in (you guessed it) China. Each spice represents one of the five elements: metal, earth, wood, water, and fire. Traditional Chinese medicine suggests that imbalances of the five elements within our bodies can cause illness. Five-spice powder was originally created to help restore balance to our bodies.

I've found it is fantastic on sweet potatoes, on roasted chicken, or as a meat rub. It's particularly yummy mixed with a bit of honey and orange zest, then drizzled over a pork roast before baking. Once you get the knack for making this recipe, you can customize with your favorite flavors—I like extra Szechuan peppercorns in my mix. In China, the recipe varies from region to region and from household to household based on the preferences of the chef.

INGREDIENTS

- 1 tablespoon anise powder
- 1 1/2 teaspoons ground Szechuan peppercorns (substitute regular black peppercorns)
- 1 1/2 teaspoons ground fennel
- 1 1/2 teaspoons cinnamon
- 1 1/2 teaspoons ground cloves
- 1 1/2 teaspoons salt (optional sixth spice)

INSTRUCTIONS

1. Combine all the seasonings, mixing well (or grinding with a mortar and pestle).
2. Place in an airtight jar.
3. Store in a cool, dry location.

As a person who travels a lot, I am privileged to taste all types of wonderful cuisines. On one lonely evening in Philadelphia, I found a little Thai restaurant near my hotel. Their special for the night was White Fish in Thai Coconut Sauce. After dinner I requested the recipe from the chef and the magic for the sauce was all about the seasoning—my own version of this memory follows. If you can't find dried lemongrass on the spice shelf, try looking for it in the tea section. Pure lemongrass tea is simply dried lemongrass leaves.

WONDERFUL WHITE FISH
IN THAI COCONUT SAUCE

 10 MINUTES YIELDS 1/4 CUP 2 1/2 HOURS YIELDS 8 SERVINGS

Coconut Thai Spice Seasoning Mix

INGREDIENTS

- 2 tablespoons coconut flake powder
- 1 teaspoon garlic powder
- 1 teaspoon salt
- 1/2 teaspoon onion powder
- 1/2 teaspoon coriander powder
- 1/2 teaspoon ground ginger
- 1 teaspoon crushed red pepper flakes
- 1 teaspoon dried lemongrass

White Fish in Thai Coconut Sauce

INGREDIENTS

- 4 limes, juiced
- 4 cloves garlic, crushed
- 2 tablespoons Coconut Thai Spice Seasoning Mix
- 2 pounds white fish, skinless and cut into 2-inch pieces

- 2 tablespoons olive oil
- 1 large onion, diced
- 4 tomatoes, chopped
- 1 can (14 ounces) coconut milk
- Salt and pepper, to taste
- 6 sprigs fresh cilantro, chopped

INSTRUCTIONS

1. Combine all the seasonings, mixing well (or grinding with a mortar and pestle).
2. Place in an airtight jar.
3. Store in a cool, dry location.

1. Mix juice, garlic, and spice mix in a bowl. Add fish and marinate for 2 hours.
2. Heat oil in pan and sauté vegetables until slightly tender.
3. Stir in coconut milk and marinade, then add fish, letting mixture simmer, covered, for about 20 minutes.
4. Salt and pepper to taste, and serve with chopped cilantro sprinkled over the top.

CHAPTER FOUR

MEDITERRANEAN
STYLE FLAVORS

in this chapter

Mediterranean flavors are from countries that touch the Mediterranean Sea. Most of the territory shares similar weather conditions which is characterized by hot, dry summer climates. A Mediterranean-style diet spans a wide variety of cultures and flavors, is predominately heavy in produce, seafood, chicken, and whole grains, and is lower in dairy and meat products. This means a Mediterranean diet can be very low in inflammation values and quite good for your chronic pain and inflammation. We often think of Spain, France, Italy, and Greece as Mediterranean countries; however, parts of Croatia, Turkey, Cyprus, Israel, Egypt, and other North African countries are included in the regional flavors as well.

Fresh herbs from this flavor palate are aromatic and include basil, cilantro, lavender, oregano, parsley, rosemary, saffron, sage, tarragon, and thyme. A few spice combinations include Italian Seasoning Mix, Herbes de Provence mix, and Mediterranean Seasoning Mix. Without a doubt, my favorite of all these flavors is fresh lavender—the aromatic oils of lavender are magical in teas, desserts, salad dressings, and in cooking fish and meat.

USE THE ZEST
FOR A TASTIER LIFE

Zest means "great enthusiasm and energy," and it is also the outer part of the peel of a citrus fruit often used as flavoring. If you hold up an orange peel, you will see an inner white pith, which is bitter and sometimes rubbery. The colorful outside of the orange peel is the zest, and it is filled with citrus oils that give it a strong aromatic value. Citrus zest is fabulous mixed in drinks and sprinkled over meats, desserts, and breads as it imparts both a taste and scent burst that truly contributes to a dish.

Dual purpose lemon zesting tools can be both a zester and a channel knife. By cutting only the colorful zest and not the white pith of a citrus, you can capture amazing flavor and color for your recipes. This type of zester enables you to create tiny zest strips or large zest strips to use as cocktail twists or to tie into bows and other shapes. Using a rasp grater also enables a smart zest. However, you can zest without a zesting tool.

ZEST A LEMON WITHOUT A ZESTING TOOL

1. Using a vegetable peeler or paring knife, slice off a super thin layer of the outer colorful part of a citrus fruit.
2. Immediately lay this peel on a cutting board with the flesh side facing up.
3. Julienne the peel into tiny little strips.
4. Turn these little strips on the sides and mince them up into little bitty pieces.
5. Rock the knife back and forth repeatedly over the strips and it will turn into a fine zest.

While citrus zest might seem an unlikely ingredient, add a generous raw pinch to your salad dressings, fresh fruit, or Chia Seed Pudding (Page 125). Want an even richer flavor? Sprinkle heavily on vegetables before or after roasting, add to riced cauliflower, or stir into sauces. Use freshly grated zest as dried zest has less flavor.

CITRUS FLAVOR ENHANCING TIPS

1. Use a squirt of citrus juice instead of a sprinkle of salt as a way to keep your salt use down.
2. Use slices of citrus with seeds removed as a flavoring ingredient by putting them over fish, chicken, or meat when roasting.
3. If adding a bit of citrus juice to a sauce, be sure to add it just before serving so the flavor isn't overpowering.
4. Lemon and lime juice have less sugar content. Squeeze a slice in your water or over your food to add flavor without a heavy amount of sugar.
5. To enhance a salad, peel a citrus, then cut all the pith off and slice only a few pith-free slices into the salad to keep it full of acidic flavor and low on sugar.

FLIPPIN' FRESH HERBS
GETTING THE MOST FUN FLAVOR

Fresh herbs can be daunting in the beginning. My first year with herbs in the garden was an interesting one as I loved to just walk by the herbs, stepping on them or brushing them gently so I could smell the aromatic oils, yet I had no idea how to prepare them. I grew up on a Midwestern farm where our primary flavorings were salt and pepper, so I had rarely used fresh herbs until I was well into adulthood.

The Scent Hint—Whether you're adding herbs to a complex stew or simply letting an herb set on the rim of your cocktail or iced tea glass, the scent is a powerful trigger to enhance flavor. Let's say you have a casserole that contains basil and lemon flavors; try sprinkling each individual serving with some slices of fresh basil and a few bits of lemon zest. When the plate is placed in front of you, you will smell the fresh flavors and your mouth will begin watering before you ever take a bite. That's the power of a scent hint.

Leaves, Please—While herb stems can be used in making stews or broths, hard, stick-like stems must be removed from a dish before serving. Primarily add leaves and softer parts of an herb to a dish and it will build a smoother consistency.

The Chiffonade Squad—Chiffonade (pronounced shif-oh-NOD) is a French technique of finely cutting or shredding leafy herbs and vegetables. Stack the leaves in a pile, rolling the leaves tightly together on a cutting board, then slice the leaves perpendicular to the roll so you create long thin strips. It makes slicing everything from spinach to basil easier and it stays in even strips when used in your recipes.

Garden Power—Growing your own herbs means you can control whether the herbs are organic. This is clearly a benefit as you can guarantee your vegetables have fewer to no chemicals added. Freshly grown and harvested herbs also have stronger taste and nutrient content. In order to extend the life of your herb plants, harvest only one third of a plant at a time, let it grow back, and harvest another third, and so on.

Buying Herbs—If you buy your herbs at a supermarket, pick the most vibrantly colored and scented product possible. No smell? Chances are the plant will taste bland as well due to long shelf storage. Ask your produce expert how long the herbs have been on the shelf and get the freshest possible. Wait until the day you need the herbs to purchase them so they have the freshest taste. Be sure to avoid soggy, limp, yellow, or dark-colored herbs because those are beginning to age and rot.

Be a Bit Snippy—When you bring your herbs home from the grocer, wash them in cold water to remove sediment and pat dry, then snip off the ends like you would do with flowers, and place them in a cup of fresh water. Save the ends for your compost or use them in stews. Store the herbs on your countertop if they have not been refrigerated in the past; once refrigerated, they need to stay refrigerated.

Storing in the Fridge—To extend the life of the herbs, you might need to refrigerate them. Wrap a wet paper towel around the stems, then place them in a bag or glass container so the ends stay damp. Cut darkened leaves off as soon as they develop to extend the life of the herbs.

LET THEM EAT FLOWERS

Flowers are such a joy, and even more so on your salad plate. Flowers are a whole food, after all, so they make a delightful addition to your recipes. While they are traditionally known as gorgeous contributions to the birthday or wedding cake, I have found them a surprisingly stunning addition to a salad. It is easy to say no to a boring salad made without zest and verve, but it is quite wonderful to say yes to a salad that is beautiful and colorful.

Below is a list of edible flowers that can be used fresh from the garden. Organic flowers are always preferred; all flowers should be washed in cold water prior to use to eliminate insects and other particles. Most edible flowers will stay fresh up to seven days if stored between dampened paper towels in the refrigerator. If they look wilted and limp when you remove them from the refrigerator, simply float them in ice water for a short time and they will come back to life.

One concern about fresh edible flowers is pollen. To avoid allergic reactions to pollen, it is suggested you remove stamens and styles from larger flowers before serving to your guests. Below is a list of lovely edible flowers; please grow them in your garden and serve them to your guests with abandon.

TYPES OF EDIBLE FLOWERS

- Anise Hyssop
- Apple Blossom
- Arugula
- Basil
- Bee Balm
- Borage
- Broccoli
- Calendula
- Chamomile
- Chervil
- Chicory
- Chives
- Chrysanthemum
- Cilantro
- Clover
- Cornflower
- Dandelion
- Daylily
- Dianthus
- Dill
- Fennel
- Fuchsia
- Garlic
- Hibiscus
- Honeysuckle
- Impatiens
- Johnny Jump Up
- Lavender
- Lemon Bergamot
- Lovage
- Marigold
- Mint
- Nasturtium
- Okra
- Oregano
- Pansy
- Passionflower
- Pea and Sweet Peas
- Primrose
- Rose
- Rosemary
- Safflower
- Sage
- Scarlet Runner Bean
- Snapdragon
- Sorrel
- Squash Blossom
- Sunflower
- Sweet Woodruff
- Violet
- Wild Onion

Want to win the hearts of your friends and family? Make your own secret formula vinaigrette dressing. Once you build your favorite flavor combinations into a to-die-for dressing, your guests will beg you for the recipe. I like to shake up all my dressings using a stainless steel shaker with lid and pour spout for Mason jars.

Flavor swapping is possible when using spice combinations with vegetables and chicken, and the following recipe is also a flavor swapping technique where you secretly add in your own magical ingredient to create a custom one-of-a-kind dressing. It is unique, which will make it memorable and amazing at your dinner table. And remember—it's secret because it is ALL YOURS!

FLAVOR SWAP VINAIGRETTE

10 MINUTES

YIELDS 1/4 TO 1/2 CUP

INGREDIENTS

- 3 tablespoons extra-virgin olive oil (or your favorite cold-pressed oil)
- 1 1/2 tablespoons vinegar (use any variety you prefer)
- Salt and freshly ground black pepper, to taste

INSTRUCTIONS

1. Combine the olive oil, vinegar, salt, pepper, and all your favorite ingredients in a food processor or blender and whirl them together lightly. If you prefer chunkier vinaigrette, simply whisk or shake all the preferred ingredients until incorporated just before serving over your favorite salad or using as a marinade.
2. Mixture keeps in the refrigerator for a little over a week.

OPTIONAL INGREDIENTS

- 2 tablespoons freshly chopped herb of choice
- 2 tablespoons tahini
- 2 tablespoons crushed ripe tomatoes
- 2 tablespoons minced olives and/or capers
- 1 tablespoon seasoning mix (whichever seasoning mix recipe your heart desires)
- 1 tablespoon citrus juice

- 1 tablespoon grated, fresh horseradish
- 1 crushed and minced garlic clove (or more, go crazy)
- 2 teaspoons grated ginger
- 2 teaspoons finely chopped scallions, any kind
- 1 1/2 teaspoons mustard, any kind
- 1 teaspoon poppy or other seeds

- A few heavy shakes of sriracha or a dash of red pepper flakes
- Pinch celery seed
- Petals from your favorite edible flower
- 1/2 avocado, puréed or smashed
- 1/2 teaspoon to 1 tablespoon local honey
- 1/2 cup coconut cream

When I flew to Rome to visit my daughter a few years ago, I was surprised to learn that Italian seasoning, as Americans know it, does not exist on the Italian plate. A bit of rosemary here and there, or a tad of oregano or garlic, but the idea of a large quantity of flavorings combined to be one specific Italian seasoning is not really Italian in itself. Italians prefer the food to taste "like the food" in my experience, where we Americans—me included—prefer strong over-the-top flavors. All the herbs used in the Italian Seasoning Mix are distinctly Mediterranean and I love Italian Seasoning Mix in everything from tomato sauce to marinades. I especially love a heaping tablespoon sprinkled over mixed vegetables with a drizzle of olive oil.

RICED CAULIFLOWER
ITALIAN FLAVOR SWAP FRITTER

 10 MINUTES   YIELDS 1/2 CUP   15 TO 20 MINUTES   YIELDS 4 SERVINGS

Italian Seasoning Mix

INGREDIENTS

- 2 tablespoons basil
- 2 tablespoons marjoram
- 2 tablespoons oregano
- 1 tablespoon rosemary
- 1 tablespoon thyme
- 1 1/2 teaspoons garlic powder

Riced Cauliflower Fritter

INGREDIENTS

- 1 head raw cauliflower, shredded
- 5 carrots, shredded
- 1 cup peas
- 1 egg
- 1/4 cup almond flour
- 2 tablespoons coconut flour
- 2 tablespoons Italian Seasoning Mix, divided (or swap in your favorite seasoning mix)
- 2 tablespoons coconut oil, divided
- Salt and pepper, to taste

INSTRUCTIONS

1. Combine all the seasonings, mixing well (or grinding with a mortar and pestle).
2. Place in an airtight jar.
3. Store in a cool, dry location.

1. Combine vegetables and microwave until tender. Place vegetables on tea towel and dry vegetables, squeezing out as much moisture as possible.
2. Place vegetables, egg, flours, and 1 tablespoon seasoning mix in a large bowl; mix well.
3. Heat 1 tablespoon coconut oil on medium-high heat and swirl around pan.
4. Form vegetable mixture into patties and place into hot pan.
5. Cook approximately 3 minutes on each side, or until browned, adding more oil to the pan if necessary.
6. Salt and pepper, then sprinkle with remaining seasoning mix.
7. Serve warm.

HERBES DE PROVENCE
SEASONING MIX

10 MINUTES

YIELDS 1/2 CUP

When I am indecisive about what flavor swap to use for my evening meal (there are so many choices after all), my go-to swap is always Herbes de Provence Seasoning Mix. This seasoning originated in the Provence region of France, known for hot summers and incredibly savory herbs that are fabulous in stews and grilled foods. Believe me, I'm not an expert in French cuisine, but I adore the flavor combination of Herbes de Provence.

Over the centuries, Provençal cuisine traditionally used all sorts of fresh herbs, but early recipes did not include lavender. Modern recipes for Herbes de Provence vary, however, with recipes consistently containing lavender, and I find you lose a lot of aroma and flavor without the addition of lavender. I add it to my seasoning mix and sometimes add a little extra. Delicious!

Try adding 2 tablespoons Herbes de Provence Seasoning Mix to the cooking oil called for in a recipe at least an hour or so before you start dinner. Then add the oil to your pan, heat, and cook vegetables or meat until almost done. Wow! What a delicious flavor. Simply toss 1 or 2 tablespoons in your flavor swaps for chicken, fish, meat, and vegetables for a delicious experience for your palate.

INGREDIENTS

- 2 tablespoons thyme
- 2 tablespoons marjoram
- 1 tablespoon chopped fresh rosemary
- 1 tablespoon savory
- 1 1/2 teaspoons lavender flowers
- 2 teaspoons dried orange zest
- 1 teaspoon ground fennel

INSTRUCTIONS

1. Combine all the seasonings, mixing well (or grinding with a mortar and pestle).
2. Place in an airtight jar.
3. Store in a cool, dry location.

The label on the jar reads "Mediterranean Seasoning"

MEDITERRANEAN LEMON
SEASONING RUB

10 MINUTES

YIELDS 1/4 CUP

Want to taste the Mediterranean? This seasoning mix and rub is an amazing way to prompt thoughts of the Greek coastline and sunny days. I have made this seasoning mix with dried ingredients and stored it for lengthy periods of time, pulling it out for a taste of the coast in my flavor swaps. Great as a dry rub, it is also lovely in soups and stews.

If you create this mix with fresh ingredients, not dry, you will have a scent and flavor sensation that is totally over the top. Before baking, stuff a chicken with lemon, then mix the fresh version of this rub with 1/2 cup olive oil and rub over the chicken before you roast it. It is one of my favorite ways to bake chicken, and it's easy to put together.

Use either dried or fresh ingredients in this mixture.

INGREDIENTS

- 2 tablespoons lemon zest
- 1 tablespoon rosemary
- 1 tablespoon basil
- 1 tablespoon oregano
- 1/2 teaspoon black pepper
- 1/2 teaspoon salt

INSTRUCTIONS

1. Combine all the seasonings, mixing well (or grinding with a mortar and pestle).
2. If you are using dry ingredients, place all ingredients in an airtight jar and store in a cool, dry location.
3. If using fresh ingredients, use within a day or two.

PART TWO

BREAKFAST MENU

Breakfast recipes that break from the traditional and fuel your energy for the day.

Americans might be shocked to know that breakfast around the world does not feature doughnuts, sugary cereals, or toaster pastries. It is said that breakfast is the most important meal of the day, and I tend to agree. When I eat breakfast, I feel better and more energetic. The American breakfast habit of mostly sugar in the morning is so prevalent that I am often questioned about what I recommend for breakfast for an anti-inflammatory food plan.

Mostly I eat eggs for breakfast, often I include a piece of no-grain quick bread, or have fruit and nuts, warm soup in the winter, or eat leftovers from the previous night's dinner. There is no rule that says you HAVE to eat pancakes and doughnuts for breakfast—I give you permission to think outside the proverbial box of cereal and try something different, marvelous, and flavorful.

People around the world eat all kinds of foods for breakfast. A sampling follows; some are quite healthful, and I encourage you to experiment with your own breakfast fare.

BREAKFASTS FROM AROUND THE WORLD LOOK A LITTLE LIKE THIS

Japan—A traditional breakfast might include miso soup, rice, pickled vegetables, and fish or an omelet.

United Kingdom—A traditional English breakfast is large and may include eggs, sausage, bacon, beans, mushrooms, and a cooked tomato, for instance.

Germany—Germans often eat cold meats and cheese with bread and jam.

India—For the first meal of the day, you might find a tray filled with chutneys, dips, and dosa bread.

Jamaica—An island resident might have scrambled ackee (a type of fruit), plantains, salted fish, and fresh fruit.

Mexico—Huevos rancheros with cheese and beans on tortillas fit the bill.

Korea—You might find soup, rice, kimchi, and some fish or beef on the breakfast menu.

Sweden—Residents often opt for an open-faced sandwich with fish, cold cuts, cheese, mayonnaise, and vegetables.

CHAPTER FIVE
GRAIN-FREE
BREAD & TORTILLA RECIPES

──────────── *in this chapter* ────────────

Grain-free, dairy-free breads, muffins, tortillas, and crackers can be absolutely delicious and there are several yummy recipes in this chapter for you to explore. Eating an occasional single serving of one of these recipes made from ingredients other than grain is easy if you prepare the breads, then freeze them so you can pull out a single serving when you want one. I've also created a list of no-grain tortilla ideas; some are made from vegetables, which makes it easy to count on the "vegetable" side of your plate.

DEFINING GLUTEN-FREE, GRAIN-FREE, AND WHOLE GRAIN

1. What is Gluten-Free? Gluten is a sticky protein found in different types of foods and condiments, particularly those containing grains such as wheat, rye, barley, spelt, and kamut. Gluten gives bread and pastries their ability to stretch and rise. Oats and corn are naturally gluten-free; however, they can be contaminated with gluten during processing and so must be assumed to contain gluten unless the packaging certifies it is gluten-free. Items used in baking that can be assumed to be gluten-free include brown rice, buckwheat, jasmine rice, millet, quinoa, teff, amaranth, wild rice, and nut flours such as coconut and almond flour.

2. What is Grain-Free? Grain-free literally means to eliminate all grains (including corn, rice, wheat, oats, and barley) from a food or food product. A grain-free diet is also a gluten-free diet because all grains are removed from the diet, even those distinctly listed as gluten-free such as rice, millet, and amaranth. Living a grain-free lifestyle does not mean you are consuming a lower carbohydrate food plan as you can still eat grain-free breads, crackers, and tortillas, all of which might be high in healthy, complex carbohydrates. Breads without grains generally replace grains with plant-based complex carbohydrates such as starchy vegetables, cassava flour, coconut flour, almond flour, tapioca flour, arrowroot powder, and sunflower seed flour.

3. What is Whole Grain? Whole grain breads and other products use every part of the grain including the germ and bran. Ultra-processed grains remove all but the endosperm, which is the starchy material that helps hold the food product together. Whole-grain foods are higher in fiber content than refined grains and also hold more minerals and vitamins.

How do you know what products are whole grain or grain free? READ THE LABELS. Whole-grain products usually say "100% whole grain." Grain-free products will have plant-based flours listed rather than grain flours. Reading labels for all products is critical to help eliminate potentially inflammatory- or allergen-oriented ingredients.

Prepare some of the breads, tortillas, and crackers and see what foods your body will tolerate. If you feel inflamed after trying a new ingredient or going back to grains, pull back and do not eat the trigger foods. When you can reintroduce whole grains, do so slowly and in moderation. You might not be able to reintroduce grains for years, or you might be able to reintroduce within weeks. Test it out. Remember that eating well for your inflammation means that sometimes less is more; eating grains three times a day when you are first reintroducing the food might cause rejection, so focus on small portions at first. With your "all things in moderation" sign held high above your head, march into this chapter with gusto.

Because grain-free flour, such as almond or coconut flours, does not have gluten, it can taste flat and inconsistent in recipes if used alone. Gluten is the magical substance that enhances the elastic texture of breads, cakes, and pastries and enables them to rise properly. Mixing flours and starches to create this grain-free substitute works well.

Grain-free flours can be quite expensive. A thrifty choice is to make up a batch of this flour mix and keep it sealed tight in the cabinet for easy access. Simply replace the wheat flour in recipes with your grain-free flour. Grain-free breads will never be a traditional raised bread; however, I have found you can bake with this grain-free flour mix and experience better success, as long as you are not expecting a perfect replica of the original food.

This grain-free flour is a great go-to as you begin exploring grain-free breads and muffins. However, sometimes the other ingredients in a recipe, the altitude, or the moisture content can affect the grain-free baking experience. Therefore, experiment with your recipes and find what works best for you. Let the experiments begin!

ALL-PURPOSE
GRAIN-FREE FLOUR

15 TO 20 MINUTES

YIELDS APPROXIMATELY 6 CUPS

INGREDIENTS

- 3 cups almond flour (or a seed flour if you need a tree-free option)
- 1 1/2 cups arrowroot (or potato starch)
- 3/4 cup coconut flour
- 3/4 cup tapioca starch

INSTRUCTIONS

1. Sift together all the ingredients (I like sifting it twice in order to make sure everything is well incorporated).
2. Store in an airtight jar.

BREAD CRUMB ALTERNATIVES

Lentil Krispies—Lentil krispies are lentils formed into little crisps. Crush them and they can be used in place of bread crumbs. Leave them whole and they make a great cereal or crunchy topping for soups and side dishes. (See Page 219 for ordering information.)

Almonds—Ground almonds are great bread crumb material. Grind in the food processor or buy pre-ground.

Coconut or Almond Flour—Coarsely ground nut flours make excellent bread crumbs.

Sesame or Flaxseeds—These are nutritious and good when used as an outer coating on fish and meats.

When I was growing up on a farm in Indiana, my grandma used to make the fluffiest biscuits. She would serve them with an enormous dollop of her homemade grape jelly, and, on summer mornings, I would sit on the front steps eating a biscuit and listening to the crickets.

I especially love herbed biscuit recipes, and this delight is really intended to be a flavor swap for you, so you can add your own touch. I typically add Herbes de Provence Seasoning Mix (Page 77) to the mixture. You may want to flavor swap your favorite seasoning mix recipes or use fresh chopped herbs in the recipe as it tastes yummy any way you bake it.

HERBED BISCUITS

45 TO 60 MINUTES

YIELDS 12 BISCUITS

INGREDIENTS

- 2 cups All-Purpose Grain-Free Flour (Page 85), plus more for cutting dough
- 2 teaspoons baking powder (aluminum-free)
- 1 tablespoon seasoning mix (or more if you want extra flavor)
- 1 teaspoon baking soda
- 1/2 teaspoon salt
- 5 tablespoons cold butter or ghee (if you can't have butter or ghee, substitute an equal amount of cold mashed avocado or coconut oil)
- 1/2 cup dairy-free milk
- 1 teaspoon citrus juice
- 2 eggs, whisked

INSTRUCTIONS

1. Heat oven to 400 F and line a baking sheet with parchment paper.
2. Combine the dry ingredients in a large bowl.
3. Add the cold butter to the dry ingredients and cut in using a fork until the mix is the consistency of coarse meal.
4. In a separate bowl, mix together the milk and juice. Let set for 5 minutes, then add the eggs, mixing gently until well combined.
5. Add liquid ingredients to dry ingredients, mix well. Allow wet mixture to rest for 5 to 10 minutes.
6. Dip an ice cream scooper into extra All-Purpose Grain-Free Flour, lightly shake off excess flour, then use the scooper to cut out about 1/4 cup biscuit dough and drop onto baking sheet.
7. Bake 12 to 15 minutes, until the tops of the biscuits turn golden brown.
8. Cool and serve.

When I first tried a bite of a cauliflower crust, I was downright shocked at how good it tasted. As a person who has been grain-free for many years, the ability to enjoy a bit of crunchy crust feels decadent. Of course, this bread-like creation is good as an all-around pizza crust, and it also makes a great base for appetizers (instead of crackers), functions as breakfast toast, and works as a slice of sandwich bread for your avocado toast or breakfast sandwiches (or any sandwich for that matter).

I have made dozens of cauliflower pizza crusts and flat breads, both with fresh cauliflower and frozen cauliflower, and I cannot tell the difference in taste or consistency between the two. With this in mind, I recommend you use any of the frozen, riced, no-extra-ingredients-added cauliflower found in the freezer aisle of your grocer's. Simply thaw the frozen riced cauliflower, then drain and squeeze out all the liquid once the cauliflower hits room temperature. If you use fresh cauliflower, follow the directions in the Basic Riced Cauliflower recipe (Page 35), cooking the cauliflower in advance of draining and squeezing. This freezes fabulously, so make big batches to save for meal prepping.

CAULIFLOWER
FLAT BREAD OR PIZZA CRUST

60 TO 80 MINUTES

YIELDS 4 SERVINGS

INGREDIENTS

- 2 packages (12 ounces each) frozen riced cauliflower, thawed (or 2 pounds cauliflower, cooked and riced)
- 3 tablespoons coconut flour
- 2 tablespoons avocado oil
- 1 teaspoon Italian Seasoning Mix (Page 75), or your choice of flavor swap seasoning mix
- 1 egg, beaten
- 1/2 teaspoon salt
- Ground pepper, to taste

BREAKFAST TOPPINGS

- Pizza sauce or olive oil
- Over-easy or scrambled eggs
- Ground turkey or chicken sausage
- Grilled diced onions and peppers
- Fresh basil, tomatoes, or olives

INSTRUCTIONS

1. Heat oven to 400 F. Either oil a baking sheet or line it with parchment; set aside.
2. Add riced cauliflower to a thin dishtowel, then twist at the top and start squeezing until all the moisture is pressed out.
3. Combine all the ingredients.
4. Press the dough onto the parchment paper, top with more parchment paper, and roll to a thickness of about 1/4 to 1/2 inch.
5. Bake about 30 minutes, checking to see if it is evenly browned. If not, flip the crust over and bake another 15 minutes or so, if you are able (if not, no worries).
6. Slice and serve as bread or breadsticks. If using for an appetizer, breakfast pizza, or traditional pizza, add the toppings to the crust and bake an additional 5 to 10 minutes.

This grain-free quick bread is a little bit of heaven. I was inspired to throw in lavender and lemon when I visited a lavender field in Oregon a few seasons ago and tasted lavender cookies for the first time—lavender can be very aromatic. This delightful quick bread flavor combination works for breakfast and also functions as dessert for high tea as well. Yummy!

LUSCIOUS
LEMON LAVENDER
QUICK BREAD

65 TO 70 MINUTES

YIELDS 8 TO 10 SERVINGS

INGREDIENTS

- 1 cup coconut flour
- 6 eggs, whisked
- 1/4 cup maple syrup
- 1/4 cup melted coconut oil
- 1 teaspoon lemon juice

- 2 teaspoons lemon zest
- 2 teaspoons dried lavender
- 1/2 teaspoon ground Pumpkin Pie Seasoning Mix

- 3/4 teaspoon baking soda
- 1 1/2 cups shredded squash, tightly packed, squeezed, and drained

INSTRUCTIONS

1. Heat oven to 350 F. Line a 9-by-5-inch loaf pan with parchment paper; set aside.
2. In a large bowl, combine the coconut flour, eggs, maple syrup, oil, lemon juice and zest, lavender, seasoning mix, and baking soda.
3. Stir in the shredded squash.
4. Place mixture in the prepared loaf pan, and bake for 50 to 60 minutes. Test with a toothpick to determine if center is dry and done.
5. Store in refrigerator. This bread is super-moist, so I store individual slices, then take out one at a time for toasting; great served with Smash Jam (Page 126).

PUMPKIN PIE SEASONING MIX

10 MINUTES
YIELDS 2 TABLESPOONS

- 1 tablespoon cinnamon
- 1/4 teaspoon ground ginger
- 1/2 teaspoon nutmeg
- 1/2 teaspoon allspice powder
- 1/8 teaspoon clove powder

Pumpkin pie spice is the quintessential pie seasoning, yet it is great in breads, muffins, or cookies. I use it often for quick breads and love the complexity it gives to warm spiced nuts or grain-free pancake batter.

SMARTY PANTS TORTILLA AND BREAD SUBSTITUTE IDEAS

Cabbage or Collards—Steam or roast individual leaves or several leaves stacked together, then use the cooked leaves as tortillas (see Cabbage Leaf Shell recipe, Page 181).

Egg Wrap—Make a tortilla from an egg (see Eggy Crepes and Fantastical Fillers recipe, Page 119)

Jicama—Jicamas look like large potatoes, with the texture of a radish. Using a sharp knife, peel a jicama, then slice it into the thinnest, widest slices you can. It's delicious as a wrap or when used as a flat tostada.

Lettuce—Use any type of lettuce in whole leaf form as a wrap.

Sweet Potato Toast—Slice large sweet potatoes to 1/2-inch thickness, then place in toaster. Toast the slices 3 to 4 times. Another technique is to roast the slices for 20 minutes at 350 F; they make a great sandwich wrap.

Tomatoes—Slice a wide tomato in half and place the protein or meat in the middle.

GRAIN-FREE
RANCH HAND TORTILLAS

25 TO 30 MINUTES

YIELDS 6 TORTILLAS

My mother-in-law taught me how to make flour tortillas when I was first married. I remember there being a lot of rolling pin action; the result was magnificent and we would eat the tortillas as fast as we made them, hot and while standing over the stove in the kitchen. This is an adaptation of my dear mother-in-law's recipe and is worth the effort if you are craving more traditional tortillas. One fair warning—these are best served fresh and do not store well as they do not retain the fresh-from-the-skillet taste the next day.

INGREDIENTS

- 1 cup All-Purpose Grain-Free Flour (Page 85) or cassava flour
- 1 teaspoon Ranch Dressing Seasoning Mix (optional) (Page 49)
- 1/2 teaspoon salt
- 3 tablespoons avocado oil
- 1/2 cup cold water

INSTRUCTIONS

1. Place dry ingredients in large bowl. Add oil and cold water, combine, then knead into a pliable dough, adding more cold water if necessary.
2. Divide the dough into 6 even portions and roll each into a ball.
3. Heat a flat griddle or skillet (preferably cast iron) over medium-high heat.
4. Place a piece of parchment paper on the bottom of a tortilla press. Place a dough ball on top of the parchment, and place another piece of parchment over the top of the dough. Press down gently to flatten the ball of dough. It might take two presses to form a round tortilla.
5. Lower the heat to medium.
6. Peel off one side of the parchment and drop the uncooked tortilla into the skillet.
7. Cook about 60 seconds until you start to see bubbles forming in the dough and the dough is showing golden brown areas. Flip over and cook for about another 30 seconds.
8. Place the tortilla in a dishcloth to cool.
9. Repeat until all tortillas are cooked, then immediately serve hot.

THAT'S JUST NUTS
PUMPKIN MUFFINS

UP TO 50 MINUTES

YIELDS UP TO 18 MUFFINS

These delicious muffins are yummy fresh out of the oven or frozen and taken out later for breakfast or anytime. The orange zest and balsamic vinegar combine for the secret kicker and you can sprinkle the fresh-out-of-the-oven delights with additional orange zest for a terrific scent hint. I serve these with Chia Seed Pudding & Berries (Page 125) and coffee for a great morning picker-upper.

INGREDIENTS

- 1 cup coconut flour
- 2 tablespoons Pumpkin Pie Seasoning Mix (Page 91)
- 1 teaspoon baking soda
- 6 eggs, whisked
- 1/2 cup melted coconut oil
- 1 cup pumpkin purée
- 4 tablespoons maple syrup
- 1 teaspoon balsamic vinegar
- 2 teaspoons fresh orange zest
- Nuts and fresh blueberries as toppings

INSTRUCTIONS

1. Heat oven to 350 F. Line 2 or 3 standard muffin tins with 18 paper liners; set aside.
2. In a large bowl, combine the dry ingredients with the eggs until evenly mixed.
3. Stir in coconut oil, pumpkin purée, maple syrup, balsamic vinegar, and orange zest.
4. Divide evenly across all muffin pans. Add desired toppings.
5. Bake for 20 to 25 minutes, until golden brown.

OPEN YOUR MOUTH
SAYS-A-ME SEED
CRACKERS

90 MINUTES

YIELDS 4 PANS OF CRACKERS

My grandma made a snack she called Dilly Crackers by putting a whole bunch of dill all over soup crackers, and it reminded me of watching fireflies on summer evenings and of Indiana sweet tea. Trying to imitate Grandma's genius Dilly Crackers, I adapted the delicious insanity of a sesame cracker recipe. Make it in bulk—trust me on this—as your whole family will fall in love. These crackers store well. Just place them in a sealed container, no need to refrigerate.

INGREDIENTS

- 2 cups almond flour
- 5 tablespoons sesame seeds
- 1 tablespoon Ranch Dressing Seasoning Mix (Page 49)
- 1 teaspoon dried dill
- 1/2 teaspoon baking soda
- 1/2 teaspoon salt
- 1/8 teaspoon cracked black pepper (or more; go crazy)
- 2 large eggs, beaten
- 4 tablespoons Ranch Dressing Seasoning Mix, divided
- Salt and freshly cracked pepper, to taste

INSTRUCTIONS

1. Heat oven to 350 F. Place parchment paper—cut to fit—in a large sheet pan; set aside.
2. Place first seven ingredients in a bowl, stirring until well mixed.
3. Add eggs and mix until the ingredients hold together in a ball.
4. Lay 1/4 of the dough in the center of the parchment-lined sheet pan; cover with another sheet of paper. Using a rolling pin, roll dough out to a very thin layer, but not translucent.
5. Pull top sheet off and cut into even-sized crackers with a sharp knife. Sprinkle uncooked crackers with 1 tablespoon seasoning mix, salt, and freshly cracked pepper.
6. Bake in oven for 15 minutes (or until browned well).
7. Repeat the process with the rest of the dough.
8. Let cool and serve.

CHAPTER SIX

GRAIN-FREE
CEREAL & BREAKFAST
BAR RECIPES

— *in this chapter* —

Commercially produced cereal is filled with sugar, grains, and a lot of chemicals, although when it was originally invented and packaged, the intention was to be more healthful and less processed. In fact, the first packaged cereals were served regularly at sanitariums to help the health of the patients. Dr. John Harvey Kellogg developed cornflakes in the 1890s and began selling tons of the stuff because it was an easy-to-make convenience food that did not require cooking. Before long, thanks to highly addictive sugar and aggressive advertising, the cereal industry expanded into what it is today. This success is partly brought on by our morning habits—people like doing the familiar and eating similar things as a part of that morning habit, but we are also in a hurry. We rush to work, we do not have time for a detailed morning routine, so we want faster and faster food.

Tragically, this often leads us to start our days with ultra-processed foods. How can we find our way back to eating more whole foods in the morning, essentially breaking our morning habits and starting something new? If you are reading this cookbook, you have already begun the process of discovering whole foods.

If you are looking for a quick breakfast or are craving cereal for your morning repast, and you want something with more whole-food components that will help your body lower its inflammation levels, there is an easy answer in the grain-free cereal, muesli, and breakfast bar recipes found in this chapter. Delicious as a snack or as a protein helping, most grain-free cereals feature nuts, seeds, and naturally chewy ingredients to satiate even the most passionate cereal lover. Slow down and eat a full breakfast whenever possible, and use these cereal treats as a smart component of your anti-inflammatory, whole-food plan.

NUT-TASTIC
PECAN GRANOLA

35 MINUTES

YIELDS 4 SERVINGS

If you walk into my kitchen when this blueberry pecan granola is baking, you will swoon from the delicious smells drifting from the oven. Are you missing some serious "chew" in your grain-free food plan? Nuts, blueberries, and coconut build an incredibly chewy foundation that is pleasantly satisfying.

Besides being a great cereal for your breakfast routine, it is also a wonderful grain-free appetizer, particularly during the holidays when berries and nuts cover the tables at family gatherings. This recipe has a fair amount of sugar in the form of honey. However, you can certainly leave out the honey or reduce the amount. I like this mixed with a muffin (especially a That's Just Nuts Pumpkin Muffin, Page 95) broken up in a bowl with a tall cup of coffee on the side.

INGREDIENTS

- 1 teaspoon pure vanilla extract
- 3 tablespoons olive oil (or other oil of your choice)
- 2 tablespoons honey
- 2 cups pecans
- 1 cup dried blueberries or cranberries (no sugar added)
- 1/2 cup pumpkin seeds
- 1 cup unsweetened coconut flakes
- 1/4 cup slivered almonds (or Lentil Krispies, Page 219)
- 1 teaspoon Pumpkin Pie Seasoning Mix (Page 91)
- 1 teaspoon salt

INSTRUCTIONS

1. Heat oven to 350 F. Grease a baking sheet; set aside.
2. In a small bowl, combine vanilla, oil, and honey (measure the oil first and the honey will slide easily from the measuring spoon).
3. Place remaining ingredients in a large bowl, mixing well. Pour liquid ingredients over mixture in large bowl and toss to coat.
4. Spread granola on the prepared baking sheet and bake for 20 minutes.
5. Allow to cool, then break apart, and store in a dry container.
6. Serve alone as a treat or break apart a batch of That's Just Nuts Pumpkin Muffins (Page 95), mix in granola and some fresh blueberries, then heat in the microwave for a minute and serve.

CUCKOO FOR
COCONUT PORRIDGE

20 MINUTES

YIELDS 3 TO 4 SERVINGS

One of the things I miss from my childhood is a good ol' fashioned bowl of oatmeal. I've been trying to recreate it for years now and think I've finally come across a recipe that will tempt your taste buds with its warm, rich, and satisfying flavor. If you like a lot of crunch, add a generous portion of crunchy toppings.

INGREDIENTS

- 3 tablespoons coconut flour
- 4 tablespoons unsweetened shredded coconut
- 1 cup almond milk
- 1 cup sliced or crushed nuts (optional)
- 2 tablespoons almond butter or sunflower seed butter
- 1 teaspoon Pumpkin Pie Seasoning Mix (Page 91)
- 1 teaspoon maple syrup (optional)
- Dash of salt
- Toppings: nuts, dried fruit, Lentil Krispies (Page 219), berries, and/or almond milk

INSTRUCTIONS

1. Throw everything in a saucepan on medium heat, stirring well.
2. Raise heat and bring to a simmer for 3 to 5 minutes, stirring often. Watch carefully so the mixture doesn't scorch.
3. Remove the saucepan from the stove when the desired thickness is achieved, and allow the mixture to set up a bit.
4. Serve warm with toppings.

THE KITCHEN SINK
MUESLI

10 MINUTES

YIELDS 10 TO 12 SERVINGS

This muesli recipe has pretty much everything but the kitchen sink. Being coconut heavy, this is a chewy treat and perfect with almond or coconut milk drizzled over as you would do with cereal. The mixture adds some lovely chew to Chia Seed Pudding (Page 125) or makes quite a showy topper on homemade grain-free quick breads, particularly if you roast the muesli lightly just before serving. Add an optional flavor swap seasoning mix for some extra oomph.

INGREDIENTS

- 2 cups unsweetened shredded coconut
- 1 cup walnut pieces
- 1 cup chopped dates
- 1 cup chopped dried pineapple
- 1/2 cup pumpkin seeds
- 1/2 cup sunflower seeds
- 1/2 cup sesame seeds
- 1/2 cup sliced almonds
- 1/4 cup hemp hearts
- 1/4 cup chia seeds
- 2 tablespoons Pumpkin Pie Seasoning Mix (Page 91) or Curry Spice Seasoning Mix (Page 55) (optional)
- Dash of salt (optional)

INSTRUCTIONS

1. Mix everything together in a large bowl.
2. Store in the refrigerator in a tightly sealed container.

We all want something absolutely over-the-top to serve to guests when they visit. Nutty Pizza Breakfast Pie makes a lovely presentation when served in the pie pan. While it has a bit of sugar in it (you can eliminate if you like), the smooth chewiness of the nut butter and berries is what makes this so spectacular. Serve with coffee and tea and a big hug—your family is going to love you for this spectacular and healthful breakfast pie.

NUTTY PIZZA
BREAKFAST PIE

AROUND 45 MINUTES

YIELDS 6 TO 8 SERVINGS

INGREDIENTS

- 3 cups ground mixed nuts
- 1 cup ground mixed seeds
- 2 eggs, whisked
- 1/2 cup shredded coconut
- 1/4 cup coconut oil
- 1/4 cup nut butter
- 2 tablespoons maple syrup or honey
- 1 teaspoon vanilla
- 3/4 teaspoon salt

TOPPINGS

- Nut butter (your choice and quantity you prefer)
- Fresh berries and almond slivers

INSTRUCTIONS

For the Crust:

1. Heat oven to 350 F. Grease a pie plate; set aside.
2. In a large bowl, thoroughly mix together the crust ingredients (your choice of nuts, seeds, and nut butter). Spread evenly in the prepared pie plate.
3. Bake for 20 to 23 minutes until just golden brown. (Watch carefully, do not allow it to burn.)
4. Let cool.

For the Topping:

5. Spread a layer of nut butter on top of the cooled crust. Top with berries and slivered almonds.
6. Cut in slices to serve.

CINNAMON BUN
GRAIN-FREE CEREAL

10 MINUTES

YIELDS 4 SERVINGS

Grain-free cereal is actually a combination of dried fruits, nuts, and seeds. Bird food, you say? With your favorite dairy-free milk poured over top, it's a quick breakfast. Mix this in with a seed butter or nut butter, freeze it, and slice off bits like a candy bar as an afternoon snack.

Want a flavor besides cinnamon? Perhaps one that's more savory? Substitute another spicy seasoning mix in a flavor swap and the world is yours. I love to drizzle a little ghee over the top, bake it in the oven for a few minutes so that the cinnamon scent drifts through the kitchen, and then serve it as a crunchy dessert. My favorite thing is to add Curry Spice Seasoning Mix (Page 55) and a sprinkle of cayenne for some unexpected spiciness—great as a snack when you're watching movies.

INGREDIENTS

- 1 cup pecans
- 1 cup Lentil Krispies (Page 219) or almonds
- 1 cup dried apples, chopped
- 1 cup pumpkin seeds
- 1/2 cup raisins
- 1/2 cup chia seeds
- 1 tablespoon Pumpkin Pie Seasoning Mix (Page 91), or go savory with Curry Spice or Fajita Spice Seasoning (Page 51) mixes
- 1/2 teaspoon salt

INSTRUCTIONS

1. Mix everything together in a large bowl.
2. Store in refrigerator in a tightly sealed container.

CHOCOLATE CHERRY
BREAKFAST CORDIALS

30 TO 45 MINUTES

YIELDS 10 TO 12 SERVINGS

Breakfast cordials are really energy bars in disguise. They are absolutely delightful as breakfast bites served with berries and coffee or tea. A single breakfast cordial when frozen makes a surprising post-dinner dessert. I love to freeze them in the summer and eat them occasionally as an energy snack mid-day. Put a few in your back pack as an energy bar substitute before your favorite hike and you are good to go.

Remember, too much sweetness can trigger inflammatory reactions. With the dates added to this recipe, the cordials can be a bit sweet as well as tart, so save these tasty treats for special occasion nom-nom-nom-ing.

INGREDIENTS

- 1 1/2 cups dried cherries, unsweetened
- 1/2 cup pitted dates, unsweetened
- 2 cups raw Brazil nuts (or another nut of preference)
- 1/2 cup unsweetened cocoa powder
- 1/2 cup chia seeds
- 2 teaspoons vanilla
- 1/2 teaspoon salt
- 1/2 to 1 cup water
- A bit of honey (optional)
- Unsweetened cocoa powder for rolling

INSTRUCTIONS

1. Soak the dried cherries and dates in hot water until soft; drain.

2. Use a food processor or blender to blend all the ingredients together until crumbles form. If too crumbly or dry, add water until moist enough to roll into balls (you can add a bit of honey as well if you like).

3. Roll into balls, dip in cocoa powder. Serve.

4. Store in a tightly sealed container in the refrigerator. These store well in the freezer—I prefer eating them frozen as a treat in the summer.

CHAPTER SEVEN

EGG & BREAKFAST
RECIPES

in this chapter

Back in the day, eggs were labeled the big, bad, cholesterol wolf dressed in Granny's clothing. We heard horror stories in the news about how eggs caused a greater risk of heart disease due to higher cholesterol counts. Recent scientific research is proving otherwise. Moderate egg consumption, one egg a day, is actually now encouraged by medical experts. In fact, I eat eggs almost every day and love them for breakfast, lunch, or dinner. My cholesterol is low and my doctors attribute that partially to genetics and partially to a positive diet and regular exercise.

We Americans tend to add sausage, cheese, doughnuts, and other extras to our three-egg omelets, rendering the good intentioned egg a poor choice. Eating a light dairy-free omelet with salsa and fresh vegetables and a grain-free tortilla is a lot better than layering it with lots of ultra-processed and inflammatory-causing items.

HOW TO
HARD BOIL EGGS
IN THE OVEN

45 MINUTES

YIELD VARIES

INGREDIENTS

- 1 dozen medium eggs
- Bowl of ice water

INSTRUCTIONS

1. Heat oven to 350 F (if your oven runs hot, lower to 325 F).
2. Place eggs in a paper-lined muffin tin; they won't roll around this way. Cook 30 minutes.
3. Remove from oven and plunge the eggs in ice water for about 15 minutes.
4. Gently roll the eggs on a countertop to crack, then peel.
5. Refrigerate hard-boiled eggs for 5 to 7 days.

CAULIFLOWER & EGG
CLOUDS

AROUND 40 MINUTES

YIELDS 6 TO 9 SERVINGS

Cauliflower is my favorite vegetable. I like it raw or cooked a plethora of ways. One of my absolute favorites is to roll it into a breakfast cup with an egg to make a delightfully warming breakfast. I first discovered these egg cups at Hotel del Coronado on Coronado Island near San Diego, California. I fell in love with the little egg cups the Sheerwater restaurant served on site. Yummy and super easy to prepare—I prefer the egg just lightly done so the yolk is still runny and functions as a bit of a sauce. When you have holiday guests, prepare the first half of the recipe the evening before, then add the eggs and pop the cups in the oven in the morning. Anti-inflammatory, no dairy, no grain, no sugar, and ALL GOOD!

INGREDIENTS

- 3 to 4 cups finely chopped, pre-cooked cauliflower (steam until almost cooked through)
- Olive oil
- 6 to 9 large eggs
- 2 tablespoons Herbes de Provence Seasoning Mix (Page 77) or your favorite flavor swap
- Salt and pepper, to taste

INSTRUCTIONS

1. Heat oven to 400 F. Grease cups or line cups in a muffin tin; set aside.
2. Place even portions of the cauliflower in the tin. Drizzle olive oil over the cauliflower, and bake for 20 minutes.
3. Remove the cauliflower cups from the oven, and crack an egg gently over each cup. Top each egg with a pinch of herbs and seasonings.
4. Bake for an additional 6 to 12 minutes.
5. Allow to cool and serve.

FLAVOR SWAP OMELET INGREDIENTS FROM AROUND THE WORLD

French Omelet—diced tomato, finely chopped French herbs (tarragon, parsley, chives), diced onions, crumbled cooked bacon or smoked fish, salt, and pepper

Greek Omelet—leftovers from previous evening's dinner, chicken, sautéed vegetables, garlic, oregano, salt, and pepper

Indian Omelet—diced onions, green chiles, cumin, turmeric, cilantro, salt, and pepper

Mexican Omelet—diced onions, diced peppers, diced tomato, jalapeños, black beans, chorizo sausage, avocado, cilantro, salsa, salt, and pepper

Dutch Omelet—diced onions, mushrooms, potatoes, leeks, garden peas, salt, and pepper

Western Omelet—diced onions, diced green pepper, diced uncured ham, salt, and butter

VEGETABLE FLAVOR SWAP
OMELET

10 TO 15 MINUTES

YIELDS 1 SERVING

"How can I make a REAL omelet without cheese smooshed in the middle?" I get this question a lot. It can be difficult to see the foods we have cooked for 25 years in a very particular fashion as the same food prepared another way. You have always cooked omelets with cheese, and I understand how you feel. However, on a scale of difficulty, climbing Mount Kilimanjaro is really hard, right? Keep this in mind when you find a new way to make an omelet, because pulling the cheese out of your omelet is easy. You can do this.

INGREDIENTS

- Chef's choice of herbs and vegetables (see list on previous page for suggestions)
- Chef's choice of meats
- 1 to 2 eggs
- Ghee or olive oil
- Spices and/or salt and pepper, to taste

INSTRUCTIONS

1. Chop fresh herbs and vegetables.
2. Precook meats and vegetables.
3. Crack eggs into a bowl, add a touch of water, and gently whisk eggs.
4. Begin heating the pan on medium.
5. After a few moments, add a small amount of ghee to the medium-heated skillet, swirling the ghee around until it coats the entire pan.
6. Pour eggs in the pan, watching carefully and turning heat lower if the eggs are cooking too fast.
7. Carefully pull the edge of the eggs slightly away from the outside of the pan, letting the remaining liquid flow beneath the setting eggs.
8. Add all toppings, let set.
9. Fold in the sides of the omelet, shaping it into a tube. Jiggle the omelet out of the pan onto a plate and serve with herbs sprinkled over the top.

FRIED AVOCADO, CHORIZO, AND
OVER-EASY EGGS

10 TO 15 MINUTES

YIELDS 1 SERVING

I love this spicy Southwestern-themed breakfast so much I sometimes have it for lunch and often serve it to guests for breakfast. The dish reminds me of my husband, Luis, who wooed me with fried chorizo and a smile on our first vacation together. We were married a few months later. Clearly, chorizo is the way to my heart.

This plate is absolutely terrific with a bit of lime squeezed over the whole dish. Fry a large portion of chorizo and freeze. Use it as a flavoring in other dishes in your weekly meal plan or as a quick addition to your eggs in the morning.

INGREDIENTS

- 1/4 cup chorizo sausage, fried until popping and darkened in color
- 1/2 avocado, sliced
- 2 eggs
- Oil for pan
- Salt and pepper, to taste
- Squeeze of lime (optional)
- Chopped cilantro (optional)

INSTRUCTIONS

1. In small skillet, fry chorizo or reheat until hot. Slice half an avocado into the pan and cook on both sides until golden brown. Move chorizo and avocado to a plate and set aside.

2. In the same skillet, prepare 2 over-easy eggs (or to your preferred doneness). When finished, slide eggs over chorizo and avocado, or place on the side to serve.

3. Top with salt, pepper, squeeze of lime, and cilantro.

Essentially, eggy crepes are super thin omelets. While crepes are often filled with dairy products, this version is better filled with savory ingredients. This forms a crepe-like creation that is the perfect way to hold meat mixtures without falling apart.

EGGY CREPES
AND FANTASTICAL FILLERS

10 TO 15 MINUTES

YIELDS 1 SERVING

INGREDIENTS

For the Crepe:
- 1 egg
- Water
- 1/4 teaspoon any flavor swap seasoning mix (optional)
- Salt and pepper, to taste
- Oil for pan

For the Filling (just a few ideas; create your own):
- Avocado
- Garlic
- Herbs, fresh
- Meat or sausage
- Mushrooms, sautéed
- Olive oil drizzle with heavy cracked pepper
- Olives
- Onions, grilled
- Salmon (see photo)
- Smash Jam (Page 126) or fresh berries
- Salad in a Crepe—raw lettuce or leafy greens, chopped tomatoes, and chopped herbs
- Tomatoes

INSTRUCTIONS

1. Crack open the egg in a bowl. Add a teaspoon water and seasonings; whisk until fluffy.
2. Let a sauté pan heat for a few moments on medium heat. Add oil, allow it to heat for a moment or two.
3. Pour the egg into the pan. Wave or roll the pan around until the egg thinly coats the entire bottom.
4. Let it cook until done enough to flip, then flip with a wide spatula.
5. Place fillings on top—don't overfill as the crepes should be thin.
6. Fold over as you would a traditional crepe and serve.

〜〜〜〜〜〜〜〜〜〜

- Swiss chard or other green leafy vegetables sautéed with garlic
- Vegetables, mixed, chopped, and sautéed

ROASTY-TOASTY
BRUSSELS SPROUTS & EGGS

35 TO 40 MINUTES

YIELDS 4 SERVINGS

Whenever I crave a hearty breakfast, I think of this bodacious, roast-a-licious treat. If you know you have a big day ahead, this breakfast is a filler-upper for sure. The roasted Brussels sprouts are remarkably good as a side dish to most any meat or poultry dish.

INGREDIENTS

- 1 pound Brussels sprouts, trimmed and sliced in half
- 3 tablespoons balsamic vinegar
- 2 garlic cloves, crushed
- 2 tablespoons extra-virgin olive oil
- Salt and freshly cracked black pepper, to taste
- 4 to 8 eggs
- 1 or 2 large tomatoes, sliced thin
- Chives, minced, to garnish

INSTRUCTIONS

1. Heat oven to 400 F. Line a baking sheet with parchment paper; set aside.
2. Toss Brussels sprouts with balsamic vinegar, garlic, and oil.
3. Place sprouts mixture in a single layer, cut side down, on prepared sheet. Salt and pepper generously.
4. Roast for 20 to 25 minutes, checking regularly. Brussels sprouts should be brown and crisp.
5. Meanwhile, cook 1 or 2 eggs (per serving) in your favorite style.
6. Place tomato slices on top of Brussels sprouts, then add eggs as the top layer. Garnish with chives.

ZESTY WATERCESS &
SMOKED SALMON SALAD

10 MINUTES

YIELDS 1 TO 2 SERVINGS

Salmon is a lovely and healthful fish choice for an anti-inflammatory food plan, and I eat it several times a week. Instead of heavy bagels and cream cheese, might I suggest this salad as a delightful morning breakfast choice? I usually add unsweetened ice tea with a few grain-free crackers on the side. This recipe is beautiful on a brunch table as well.

INGREDIENTS

- 2 cups raw watercress or spinach, washed and drained
- 2 teaspoons capers (optional)
- 1/2 cup Secret Spy Formula Flavor Swap Vinaigrette (Page 73) (your choice of flavors, although plain olive oil or citrus both go well with this salad)
- 1 cup thinly sliced smoked salmon
- 1 hard-boiled egg, sliced thin (optional)
- 1/4 cup pickled onions
- Salt and pepper, to taste
- Chili paste or shrimp sauce for the side (optional)

INSTRUCTIONS

1. Combine watercress, capers, and vinaigrette in 1 or 2 salad bowls (or in a larger bowl and then evenly split between 2 salad bowls). Top each serving with salmon strips, then egg (if desired), and pickled onions. Season to taste.
2. Serve fresh with spicy sauce on the side.

CHAPTER EIGHT

FRUIT RECIPES

in this chapter

A fruit can be identified as any edible fleshy product of a tree or other plant that contains a seed. Fruit of all kinds are full of natural sugars and carbohydrates, and they are also chock-full of all kinds of vitamins, nutrients, and the all-important fiber. In fact, consuming fibrous fruits and vegetables is absolutely necessary in helping to maintain gut health. A food plan filled with dietary fiber can help prevent health issues like diabetes and heart disease. Fiber also helps improve blood sugar and cholesterol levels and helps you feel fuller longer. Fruit is jam-packed with all these components.

If you consume fruit high in sugar such as bananas, pomegranates, kiwi, and grapes, it can increase your inflammatory levels causing discomfort. Whether the sugar is a natural sugar seems to make little difference to the human body, although some benefits of fruits such as their fiber levels and anti-inflammatory ingredients can make the healthfulness factor balance out.

Choosing fruit with a lower sugar value combined with a high nutrition and fiber level makes a lot of sense if you are trying to balance your sugar levels for anti-inflammatory living. Eat one whole pomegranate, for example, and expect your sugar levels to skyrocket. A single pomegranate has the equivalent of 2.9 teaspoons of sugar, even though pomegranate seeds have a lot of fiber. Therefore, it becomes a better choice to use sweeter fruits like kiwi and pomegranates in moderation.

Consume, instead, lower sugar fruit with higher anti-inflammatory qualities like berries or avocado. Fresh tomatoes are also recommended as an anti-inflammatory fruit. My favorites are berries; I have a variety of berries every day because they are high in antioxidants, nutrition, fiber, and taste, with a lower, generally speaking, sugar level. Pineapple is a bit higher in sugar levels than berries, though it is another super-power in the food world as an anti-inflammatory. Pineapple contains large quantities of fiber, manganese, and vitamin C. The pineapple also has an unusual enzyme that naturally breaks down proteins to aid digestion. Therefore, consider the pineapple an exception to the rule of avoiding higher sugar fruit.

Fruit recipes featured in this book center mostly on berries; adding pineapple and avocado to your smoothies or fruity breakfast bowls is a smart plan.

A BASIC BREAKFAST
HOW TO HARD BOIL EGGS IN WATER

10 TO 15 MINUTES

YIELD VARIES

We are all challenged to find the time to sit down for a meal in these hectic times. I truly understand that as many mornings I do not have time to actually cook a meal—I know your life is similar, so a super basic breakfast I whip up on those busy mornings is hardboiled eggs with berries and coffee. That's it. Simple. To the point. Takes about a minute to prepare if you have cooked your eggs in advance. It makes me feel as if I have had something substantial. If only all life's problems could be solved so easily.

You learned How to Hard Boil Eggs in the Oven in a previous chapter; there are other ways to boil eggs that you might prefer.

INGREDIENTS

- Between 6 to 12 eggs
- Salted water

INSTRUCTIONS

1. Place a dozen eggs (or fewer) in a saucepan filled with salted water.
2. Over high heat, bring water to a rolling boil.
3. When the water begins to boil, turn off heat and cover for 10 minutes (if you like a drier/harder cooked egg, leave simmering on low uncovered for the 10 minutes).
4. Pour eggs into a colander and run cold water over them or place them in a cold water bath for 10 to 15 minutes (this helps the eggs peel more easily).
5. Add berries on the side and eat immediately or refrigerate up to 5 days.

CHIA SEED PUDDING
& BERRIES

3 HOURS TO OVERNIGHT

YIELDS 2 SERVINGS

Twice a day I feel the need for a snack: after breakfast if I've not eaten enough and after dinner when I need a little something. Chia Seed Pudding with a few berries does the trick, leaving me feeling satisfied. It is a fantastic breakfast all by itself, and works equally well with a piece of grain-free quick bread. My nutritionist suggests making it daily or every other day, storing it in the fridge for a quick snack when you need a little somethin'-somethin'.

INGREDIENTS

- 1 cup non-dairy milk or water
- 4 tablespoons chia seeds
- 1 teaspoon maple syrup (optional)
- 1 cup washed berries or 1 cup Smash Jam (Page 126)

INSTRUCTIONS

1. Place milk, chia seeds, and maple syrup in a Mason jar or a sealable glass container. Shake like you mean it.

2. Refrigerate for 3 hours to overnight, then stir (if it's too runny for you, add more chia seeds next time; I like mine a bit thicker).

3. Serve as a yummy breakfast in the morning with berries on the bottom—a serving of chia seed pudding is about 1/2 cup.

4. Refrigerate up to 5 days.

SMASH JAM

5 TO 6 MINUTES

YIELDS 4 SERVINGS

Smash Jam was a happy accident—I left berries on an outside patio table while I was weeding. Weeding is therapy, after all, and held all my attention for several hours. When I came back to the berries, they had melted a bit in the sun. I smooshed them all together and ate them anyway. Delicious!

With a little citrus zest, the jam makes a flavorful addition to anything in which you might use traditional sugar-filled jam. For instance, serve at room temperature on a toasted grain-free biscuit or quick bread, mix in Chia Seed Pudding (Page 125), or serve hot in a bowl with chia seeds and a handful of nuts.

INGREDIENTS

- 2 pints blueberries, raspberries, blackberries, or strawberries
- 2 tablespoons orange or lemon zest
- 2 tablespoons citrus juice

INSTRUCTIONS

1. Place berries in a bowl, and smash with a fork until loosely mashed.
2. Add remaining ingredients. Mix well, and refrigerate leftovers.

MARY'S BEST BERRY
FREEZER JAM

1 OR 2 HOURS

YIELDS 4 SMALL JARS

My dear friend Mary Rosti, homesteader extraordinaire, has a jelly-and-jam-making business. She specializes in creative flavors and healthful ideas, and she made this sugar-free jam for me as an anti-inflammatory choice. It is a perfectly delicious solution for all your jam needs. A refrigerator jam, it can be used as a topping for breakfast cereals, toast, or desserts. This jam has no sugar to preserve it, getting all the sugar it needs from the fruit, so once opened, refrigerate it only for 5 to 7 days.

INGREDIENTS

- 1 cup cherries
- 1 cup strawberries
- 1/2 cup raspberries
- 1/2 Granny Smith apple, diced
- Dash of lemon juice

INSTRUCTIONS

1. Place all ingredients in a slow cooker or a heavy-bottom pot on low heat.
2. Cook, uncovered, until everything is soft; then, using a potato masher, smash the fruit to release the juices.
3. Continue cooking on low until mixture thickens. Let cool.
4. Pour mixture into small, airtight Mason jars, leaving a bit of room at the top for fruit to expand as it freezes.
5. Refrigerate for 5 to 7 days; freeze up to 4 months.

TROPICAL SUNSHINE
COCONUT CRUMBLE

25 TO 30 MINUTES

YIELDS 4 SERVINGS

Another marvelous brunch dish, this crumble can be served as a casserole if the recipe is doubled. It is sugar-free, gaining sweet and tart flavors from the fruit with a crispy and golden crust that brings a smile to your soul. Obviously it works as a hot breakfast bowl with a little dairy-free milk drizzled over the top, and the aroma from the oven almost reminds me of my childhood. The versatile Tropical Sunshine Coconut Crumble can be a pleasant grain-free, dairy-free, and sugar-free dessert.

INGREDIENTS

Bottom Layer:
- 2 cups blueberries
- 1 cup diced pineapple
- 2 tablespoons lime juice
- 1 tablespoon chia seeds
- 1 teaspoon Pumpkin Pie Seasoning Mix (Page 91)

INGREDIENTS

Crumble:
- 4 tablespoons coconut flour
- 4 tablespoons cassava flour
- 4 tablespoons shredded coconut
- 1 tablespoon crushed nuts, any variety
- 3 tablespoons coconut oil (in solid form)

INSTRUCTIONS

1. Heat oven to 350 F.

For the Bottom Layer:

2. In a bowl, mix together the bottom layer. Place in a square 9-inch baking dish, and bake for 10 minutes.

For the Crumble:

3. In a bowl, combine flours, coconut, and nuts.

4. Cut in coconut oil to make a topping with the consistency of bread crumbs.

To Combine:

5. Pull out the baking dish, spoon the crumble layer over the top of the hot blueberry mixture, and return to the oven. Continue to bake until bubbly and the crumble is lightly browned.

6. Top with additional shreds of coconut and nuts.

7. Serve hot with 1/2 cup dairy-free milk, or refrigerate and serve cold.

JAZZY GINGER PINEAPPLE ALMOND MILK
SMOOTHIE

5 TO 10 MINUTES

YIELDS 1 SERVING

Smoothies are great for breakfast. Throw raw whole foods into a blender and you have all the fiber and flavor in a convenient carry mug. Anti-inflammatory smoothies made in my kitchen are full of the healthful beneficial ingredients without the dairy and grains. The myth that seems to be prevalent is that anti-inflammatory is not flavorful. The truth is that you can add lots of flavor with some of your favorite spices and you will be LOVING your smoothies. Basil is incorporated into this recipe; it's a strong flavor ingredient for smoothies and truly takes the taste to new levels.

Start by growing some yummy fresh sweet basil for your delicious almond milk smoothie. Frozen pineapple gives your smoothie an ice-cream-like consistency. Freeze your almond milk into ice cubes for a frostier version. Use almond milk or coconut milk—both non-dairy milks work extremely well in the blender and taste delightful. This is a super delicious smoothie that is healthful as can be.

INGREDIENTS

- 1 cup frozen pineapple
- 1/2 cup almond butter
- 1 handful shredded basil
- 1 1/2 cups almond or coconut milk
- 1/2 teaspoon vanilla
- 1/2 teaspoon turmeric
- 1/4 teaspoon black pepper
- 1 teaspoon raw ginger, chopped (add more to taste; I add a bucket as I like it spicy!)

INSTRUCTIONS

1. Throw it all in a blender.
2. Blend'er up. DONE!

CHOCOLATE AVOCADO
SMOOTHIE

5 TO 10 MINUTES

YIELDS 1 SERVING

Chocolate in a healthy recipe? Yep. You can do it if you use unsweetened cocoa or cacao powder. Using avocado and frozen berries in the blender helps the ingredients firm up a bit, and you will get a super thick, extremely rich, non-dairy, vegan, note-of-decadent-chocolate smoothie. It is so thick it resembles pudding and can be used for fruit-based power bowls if you add some healthful toppings like nuts and coconut. The best part of this smoothie is that by adding Swiss chard or another leafy green vegetable, you are truly adding some strong nutritional value to the smoothie. This smoothie is filling and wonderfully satisfying.

INGREDIENTS

- 1 cup frozen berries
- 1/2 ripe avocado
- 1 handful shredded Swiss chard (or spinach)
- 2 tablespoons cocoa or cacao powder, unsweetened
- 1 1/2 cups almond or coconut milk
- 1/2 teaspoon vanilla
- 1 teaspoon raw honey (optional)

INSTRUCTIONS

1. Throw it all in a blender.
2. Blend'er up. DONE!

PART THREE

LUNCH & SNACK MENU

Lunch recipes that are simple, easy, and fill you up completely.

As a person who travels all over the world, I am often stuck in airports, convention centers, malls, and at events with no healthful lunch or snack available. This lack of healthful food is definitely a traveler's dilemma, because, if I want junk food that will throw me into inflammatory pain, I can get it in a heartbeat. Finding a solid celery stick or salad without dairy and soy can be immensely challenging. Every person who travels faces these same issues.

The secret is to be prepared. Fresh anti-inflammatory snacks and lunches are easy to pack in a purse, briefcase, or backpack. I like to use stainless steel or glass containers to avoid the chemical leaching that happens with plastics and Styrofoam. When you know you are going to be away from home, make a travel food plan that enables you to always have a healthful snack or lunch close at hand for emergencies.

Part III is all about creative and delicious lunch and snack recipes that you can make in advance to have ready at a moment's notice whenever you need a healthful nibble.

CHAPTER NINE

SALAD RECIPES

in this chapter

In defining what your food plan plate should be, keep in mind that produce—both raw and cooked vegetables especially—needs to make up at least half of your plate. Imagine a full-sized plate heaped over generously, so full that it is difficult to get a protein and other side dishes on the plate—THAT is how much salad you can have at every meal. Each and every meal, you can have at least two cups (or more) of raw vegetables, herbs, nuts, fruits, and seeds. Proteins such as chicken and fish or beans and other legumes are great additions to a salad. If you have reintroduced grains, you can also have whole grains like wild rice, quinoa, barley, and millet on your salads. The recipes in this chapter are both dairy-free and grain-free for your quick reference. This ceviche salad is tart, spicy, delicious, and filled with fresh flavors.

CRAZY ZOODLE COCONUT
CEVICHE SALAD

UP TO 4 1/4 HOURS

YIELDS 4 SERVINGS

INGREDIENTS

- 1 pound flounder or sushi grade sea bass, diced
- 1/2 cup fresh lime juice
- 1/4 cup fresh orange juice
- 1/2 red onion, sliced thin
- 2 tablespoons minced cilantro
- 1 tablespoon seeded and minced jalapeño
- 1 teaspoon lime zest
- 1 teaspoon orange zest
- 1/2 to 1 teaspoon salt
- 1 cup coconut milk
- 1/4 cup pickled onions
- Garnish: 1 cup zoodles (spiral-cut vegetable noodles; carrots, zucchini, or whatever vegetables you have available)

INSTRUCTIONS

1. Place fish, juices, onion, cilantro, and jalapeño in a glass bowl. Toss together; be sure the fish is completely covered with juices.
2. Cover and refrigerate 1 hour; fish should be white and opaque all the way through after that time.
3. Add the remaining ingredients except the garnish; return mixture to the refrigerator for an additional 2 to 3 hours.
4. Add garnish just before serving. Serve alone, with grain-free crackers, or with grain-free chips.

CRUNCHY FENNEL
STACK SALAD

UP TO 30 MINUTES

YIELDS 1 TO 2 SERVINGS

When various foods are crunchier, I call this mysterious measurement "The Crunch Factor." We need chewy and crunchy foods in our diet to help our brains and bodies feel satiated. In fact, digestion does not begin in our stomachs, it begins in our mouths. Chewing helps stimulate some of the enzymes that aid digestion and begin triggering the whole system to work properly. The Crunch Factor is important as crunchier things enable us to have a more satisfying chew.

Raw vegetables and fruits are extremely nutritious because cooking breaks down the nutrients, enzymes, and fiber naturally found in such foods. Adding two to three cups of a raw, whole-food salad at most meals can make a tremendous difference in your inflammatory reactions. One of my favorite lunches with a strong crunch factor is this fennel salad. As fennel loves dill, the Ranch Dressing Seasoning Mix (Page 49) would be a great flavor swap in this mix. Tasty and delicious, you can add a cup of any protein if you like.

INGREDIENTS

- 2 cups thinly sliced fennel
- 1 cup peeled, thinly sliced carrots
- 1 cup peeled, thinly sliced jicama
- 1 cup snow peas
- 1/2 cup premade Secret Spy Formula Flavor Swap Vinaigrette (Page 73), or your choice of flavors
- Salt and pepper, to taste
- Green onions and Italian parsley, chopped

INSTRUCTIONS

1. Mix together fennel, carrots, jicama, snow peas, and vinaigrette in a large bowl, tossing lightly.
2. Pull out larger vegetables with tongs and place on your plate. Start stacking vegetables from largest to smallest.
3. Drizzle a bit of the dressing over the top of the salad, sprinkling with crushed salt and pepper and a bit of the dry seasoning mix.
4. Top with onions and parsley before serving.

PICKLED PEAR
VEGGIE SALAD

UP TO 2 1/2 HOURS

YIELDS 1 TO 2 SERVINGS

During the hot days of July back in Indiana, my grandmother would make up a big batch of pickled cucumber and onion salad, bring out some cold fried chicken from the night before, and fill the sweet tea glasses full of ice. We would eat this delectable cold lunch on Saturday afternoons after spending all morning picking green beans and cucumbers from Grandma's garden.

Taking my grandmother's classic pickled cucumber and onion salad and changing it up a bit, I have created this pickled pear masterpiece of deliciousness. It is particularly good served with cold fried chicken or white fish as a main course; the fresh dill adds a kick of bright flavor making it a must-have summer salad.

INGREDIENTS

- 1/2 cup chopped fresh dill, or 2 tablespoons dried dill
- 1/2 cup white wine vinegar (or more if needed)
- 1/2 cup extra-virgin olive oil
- 2 teaspoons salt
- 2 cups thinly sliced cucumbers
- 1 cup peeled and julienned jicama (or white radish)
- 1 cup thinly sliced pears, skin on
- Freshly cracked black pepper

INSTRUCTIONS

1. In a small bowl, whisk together the dill, vinegar, olive oil, and salt.
2. Place the vegetables and fruit in a large bowl.
3. Pour salad dressing over and toss. Marinate for 1 to 2 hours.
4. Serve cold with a strong cracking of fresh black pepper.

HOT AND YUMMY BACON-ANZA
SPINACH SALAD

20 MINUTES

YIELDS 4 SERVINGS

A classic American salad is a spinach salad drizzled with a warm and delicious bacon dressing. Endless variations of this recipe can be found in homes and restaurants all over the country. It is utterly fantastic—an extravaganza of bacon flavor wrapped in classic yumminess.

Special Note: This dressing has a high percentage of saturated fat, which can induce inflammation in some people, making this a salad best reserved for special occasions, not every day. Watching your saturated fat intake can have a positive effect on your long-term health care.

INGREDIENTS

- 8 bacon slices, cooked and crumbled, with 3 tablespoons bacon drippings reserved
- 6 cups raw spinach, cleaned and de-stemmed
- 1 cup sliced mushrooms (optional)
- 1/2 red onion, thinly sliced
- 3 tablespoons apple cider vinegar
- 1 tablespoon Dijon mustard
- 2 teaspoons raw honey
- Salt and freshly cracked pepper, to taste
- 4 hard-boiled eggs, peeled and sliced

INSTRUCTIONS

1. Fry the bacon and drain, reserving drippings. Cool and crumble.
2. In a large bowl, combine spinach, mushrooms, and red onion; set aside.
3. Place bacon drippings in a small saucepan on low heat; whisk in apple cider vinegar, mustard, honey, salt, and pepper.
4. Add bacon and dressing to spinach mixture, tossing lightly.
5. Place sliced hard-boiled eggs on top of salad just before serving. Top with more cracked pepper.

FEISTY RAW CABBAGE
& KALE SALAD

2 TO 24 HOURS

YIELDS 4 SERVINGS

Want a last-minute salad recipe for any event, that costs less than $10, is easy to transport from your house to the big event, superfast to make, and utterly feisty and delicious? I have just the thing—a bold mustard vinaigrette, cabbage, kale, and tomato salad. To spice it up, add additional ground black pepper. It tastes better once it has marinated overnight, and you can flavor swap any of your favorite vegetables.

INGREDIENTS

- 2 cups premade Secret Spy Formula Flavor Swap Vinaigrette (Page 73)
- 2 tablespoons mustard
- 2 cups shredded cabbage
- 2 cups chopped or torn kale
- 2 cups cubed tomatoes
- 2 cups diced onions
- Salt and pepper, to taste

INSTRUCTIONS

1. In a small bowl, whisk together the vinaigrette and mustard; set aside.
2. Place all the vegetables in a large bowl.
3. Pour the salad dressing over the vegetables and toss to coat. Marinate for 2 to 24 hours.
4. Serve cold with a sprinkle of salt and a strong cracking of fresh black pepper.

SEARED TUNA
WITH SPICY GINGER MARINADE & SALAD DRESSING

ABOUT 75 MINUTES

YIELDS 2 TO 4 SERVINGS

Soy is often a major ingredient in Asian recipes, but this ingredient often triggers inflammation—and certainly my own osteoarthritis. I finally found a perfect flavor-filled, no-soy marinade that works great with fish. The bonus is a lot of delicious citrus and sesame flavor, which makes this marinade an excellent salad dressing as well. Prepare two batches of the marinade—one for your tuna marinade and a second batch for a salad dressing. I've used tuna with red seaweed as the salad; you can flavor swap salad greens and have seared tuna with romaine or Swiss chard or any leafy greens you can imagine. A great light lunch full of protein and flavor.

INGREDIENTS

- Tuna steaks
- Cooking oil

Marinade:
- 1/4 cup orange juice
- 1/4 cup lemon juice
- 3 tablespoons olive oil
- 1 teaspoon finely chopped ginger (more if you like)
- 1 garlic clove, crushed and chopped

Tuna Steak Topping:
- Sesame seeds
- Black pepper

INSTRUCTIONS

1. Mix together all marinade ingredients. Marinate tuna steaks for 1 hour.
2. Pull steaks out of marinade, pepper, and dip all sides in sesame seeds.
3. Heat cooking oil in a frying pan on high until just below smoking point—a very hot pan. Place crusted tuna in the pan for 1 minute each side. Watch carefully to be sure you do not burn the seeds.
4. Slice tuna in 1/4-inch slices on a cutting board.
5. Serve immediately over a salad of your choice.

CHICKEN BURRITO
SALAD ROLL UPS

UP TO 50 MINUTES   YIELDS 4 SERVINGS

Modern restaurants entice me with burrito salads. I love them with a passion and have found a great way to whip up a glorious chicken burrito salad—no cheese or sour cream necessary—filled with crispy crunch. Great in your lunch box as a lettuce fajita taco or roll up (use a grain-free tortilla in place of the lettuce), or eat as a salad. Yummers!

INGREDIENTS

Quick Pico de Gallo:
- 1 cup diced tomatoes
- 1/2 cup diced onions
- 1/4 cup minced cilantro
- 1 small jalapeño, minced and seeded
- Juice of 1 lime

Salad:
- 2 cups shredded rotisserie or roasted chicken
- 2 tablespoons avocado oil
- 1/2 cup diced onions
- 1 tablespoon Fajita Spice Seasoning Mix (Page 51)
- 1 cup black beans or vegetarian refried beans (optional)
- 2 cups Basic Riced Cauliflower (Page 35)
- 2 cups butter lettuce leaves (approximately 2 small heads)
- 1 whole avocado, sliced (or guacamole)
- Salt and pepper, to taste

INSTRUCTIONS

1. Combine all ingredients for pico de gallo; set aside to marinate.
2. Combine chicken, avocado oil, onions, and seasoning mix in saucepan; turn heat to low. Cook until lightly browned.
3. Heat beans until warm.
4. Prepare riced cauliflower; in a small saucepan, heat until warmed through.

To Assemble:
5. Place all ingredients out to assemble.
6. Place lettuce on plate; top with warmed beans then warmed riced cauliflower.
7. Add meat mixture on top of warmed rice. Top with pico de gallo, sliced avocado, salt, and pepper.

CHAPTER TEN

POWER BOWL STACKS

— *in this chapter* —

Power bowls have become a hot trend in the food world because they are a full meal that is nutritionally dense and easy to prepare. One fantastic advantage to building a power-bowl-style meal is it is easy-fixin' for advance meal prepping. You can easily prepare these power bowls and freeze the meat portion or refrigerate it all. Store the power bowls in a Mason jar for easy transport and simply dump the salad on a paper plate for lunch.

A FORMULA FOR AN ANTI-INFLAMMATORY
POWER BOWL

ABOUT 15 MINUTES

YIELDS 1 SERVING

Power bowls are an amazing, simple, and fun way to build a whole-food-based lunch (or breakfast or dinner, for that matter). They are convenient because you can use leftovers for a last-minute meal or build them in advance according to your meal plan. Start with a leafy green base and go from there.

For an anti-inflammatory formula, I've used the general guide of a no-grain and no-dairy approach; however, if you have reintroduced grains, no worries. You can customize the formula for your needs. Keep in mind, improvisation is encouraged, and the general formula below will get you started.

INGREDIENTS

- 1 1/2-plus cups leafy greens or raw vegetables (the base)
- 1-plus cup(s) additional vegetables
- 1/2 to 3/4 cup protein
- 1/4 cup healthy fats
- 1/2 to 3/4 cup complex carbohydrates or starchy foods (whole grains)
- Salt and freshly cracked pepper, to taste

INSTRUCTIONS

1. Place veggies in the bottom of the bowl, pile everything else on top.
2. ENJOY!

The Scotch Egg Veggie Bowl came about because of three things I happened to have in my refrigerator for lunch one day: 1) hard boiled eggs, 2) ground turkey, and 3) leftover vegetables from the night before. Combine these together and voilà! A little bit of creative magnificence. This recipe is quite easy to refrigerate for advance meal prep. Slice the Scotch eggs in half and use them on grain-free toast in the mornings for a yummy breakfast.

SCOTCH EGG
VEGGIE BOWLS

UP TO 1 HOUR

YIELDS 4 TO 6 SERVINGS

INGREDIENTS

Scotch eggs:

- 1 pound ground turkey
- 1 1/2 tablespoons Italian Seasoning Mix (Page 75), or flavor swap your favorite
- 1 tablespoon minced fresh parsley
- 1 tablespoon minced fresh garlic
- Salt and pepper, to taste
- 6 eggs, hard-boiled

Bowl (enough for one bowl):

- 2 tablespoons extra-virgin olive oil
- 2 tablespoons lemon juice
- 2 cups baby spinach
- 1 cup mixed vegetables (or leftover vegetables of any variety), roasted
- 1 cup cherry tomatoes, roasted for 20 minutes in oven at 350 F
- Salt and pepper, to taste

INSTRUCTIONS

For the Scotch eggs:

1. Heat oven to 350 F.
2. In a large bowl, combine turkey, seasoning mix, parsley, garlic, salt, and pepper.
3. Once the eggs are hard-boiled and peeled, dry off each egg with a kitchen towel.
4. Using your hands, grab a medium meatball-sized portion of the turkey mixture, flatten, and wrap it carefully around a hard-boiled egg, pressing gently until it closes on all sides.
5. Lightly brown the Scotch eggs in an cast-iron skillet, then transfer to the oven and bake for 30 minutes.

To Assemble Bowls:

6. Whisk together olive oil and lemon juice (or whip up the Secret Spy Formula Flavor Swap Vinaigrette, Page 73).
7. Toss baby spinach with salad dressing.
8. Layer mixed vegetables and tomatoes on top of spinach.
9. Cut open a Scotch egg and place on top of the salad to serve. Repeat steps 6 through 9 for each serving.

THE CARIBBEAN GOLD
PIRATE BOWL

20 MINUTES

YIELDS 1 SERVING

All hands on deck for this yummy, spicy bowl of adventure! Pirates were famous travelers of the Caribbean, and I have taken some artistic license to name this Caribbean-flavored power bowl with pirate escapades in mind. Substitute sautéed collard greens for the kale, if you want more options. I'll be seeing you on the beach for lunch. Argh, mateys, get to cookin'!

INGREDIENTS

- 1 cup thinly sliced onions
- 1 cup cubed sweet potato or butternut squash
- 1 tablespoon avocado oil
- 3/4 cup shredded rotisserie or roasted chicken
- 1 1/2 tablespoons Jamaican Jerk Seasoning Mix (Page 29) or Cajun Country Spice Seasoning Mix (Page 45)
- 1 tablespoon maple syrup
- Juice from 1 large lime
- 2 tablespoons water or broth
- 1 cup fresh young greens (your choice)
- 1 cup Basic Riced Cauliflower (Page 35)
- 1/2 avocado, sliced
- Salt and pepper, to taste

INSTRUCTIONS

1. In a skillet, over medium heat, sauté onions and sweet potato in avocado oil until onions are transparent.
2. Add chicken, seasoning mix, maple syrup, lime juice, and water. Combine and sauté until heated through; set aside.
3. Place raw greens (or precooked kale, if you prefer) in the bottom of the bowl.
4. Add riced cauliflower, then chicken mixture.
5. Top with avocado slices, salt, and pepper.

TREMENDOUS TURKEY AVOCADO
BLT BOWL

10 MINUTES

YIELDS 1 SERVING

When you taste this delicious concoction, your eyes will close in happiness. Very high in the crunch factor, this is one of my favorite bowls. By making your own dressing with freshly whipped up Ranch Dressing Seasoning Mix (Page 49), you significantly increase the flavor factor. Without a doubt, this bowl is comparable to a BLT sandwich and will garner rave reviews from your family and friends.

INGREDIENTS

- 2 tablespoons mayonnaise (soy free, grain free, dairy free)
- 1 tablespoon Ranch Dressing Seasoning Mix (optional)
- 1 tablespoon dairy-free milk
- 2 cups arugula (or iceberg lettuce)
- 4 ounces grilled or roasted turkey, sliced
- 1 cup quinoa, cooked (or Basic Riced Cauliflower, Page 35)
- 1 cup thinly sliced cherry tomatoes
- 1/2 avocado, sliced
- 1 slice bacon, cooked and crumbled
- Salt and pepper, to taste

INSTRUCTIONS

1. In a small bowl, whisk together mayo, seasoning mix, and dairy-free milk (add more dairy-free milk if you like a thinner dressing).
2. Place arugula in the bottom of a serving-sized bowl.
3. Layer on remaining ingredients.
4. Drizzle dressing over the bowl's contents, topping with crumbled bacon, salt, and pepper.

ROASTED VEGETABLE AND
TAHINI BOWL

15 MINUTES

YIELDS 1 SERVING

Roasted vegetables with tahini taste delightful. Tahini is a paste made from sesame seeds and is used throughout the Middle East and Mediterranean. Tahini is a great addition to an anti-inflammatory food plan because it is simple to make (or buy), and it is vegan, gluten-free, and has a delicious, strong, nutty taste. Adding tahini to your dressings and dishes makes everything a little bit richer in flavor.

INGREDIENTS

Tahini:

- 1 cup sesame seeds (toasted or untoasted)
- 1/4 cup avocado oil or light olive oil
- Pinch of salt (optional)

Bowl:

- 1/4 cup tahini paste
- 1 tablespoon Mediterranean Lemon Seasoning Rub (Page 79) (optional)
- 1 lemon, juiced
- 1 tablespoon balsamic vinegar
- 1 1/2 cups chopped raw spinach or your favorite greens
- 2 cups vegetables, roasted (your choice)
- 1 cup cooked quinoa, or chicken, or beans
- Salt and pepper, to taste

INSTRUCTIONS

For Tahini:

1. Place sesame seeds in food processor, and process, drizzling in the oil as you go. Process until crumbly; stop to scrape sides as necessary.
2. Store in refrigerator for up to 4 weeks; stir before serving if the oil separates.

To Assemble Bowl:

3. In a small bowl, whisk together tahini, seasoning mix, lemon juice, and balsamic vinegar; set aside.
4. Place spinach in the bottom of the bowl. Layer remaining ingredients on top, and drizzle tahini dressing over the bowl's content.
5. Salt and pepper, to taste.

ITALIAN ARTICHOKE
BOWL FROM ROME WITH LOVE

20 MINUTES

YIELDS 1 SERVING

Eating a braised artichoke heart is absolutely a must when visiting Italy. My daughter and I spent a day at La Galleria Nazionale, the National Gallery of Modern and Contemporary Art, in Rome a few years ago. We wandered the halls of art with wide eyes and open hearts, then enjoyed lunch at the museum's café. A smiling waiter delivered a mouthwatering artichoke heart dripping in olive oil to our table, and we ate it as if we were starving. Out-of-this-world delicious! This bowl captures a bit of that wonderful memory.

INGREDIENTS

- 2 tablespoons extra-virgin olive oil
- 2 tablespoons fresh-squeezed lemon juice
- 1 tablespoon Italian Seasoning Mix (Page 75)
- 1 teaspoon crushed fresh garlic (more if you prefer)
- 1 tablespoon minced fresh parsley
- 1 cup artichoke hearts, marinated in olive oil
- 2 cups arugula (or iceberg lettuce)
- 4 ounces cooked or grilled chicken, or rotisserie chicken, sliced and warmed
- 1 cup Basic Riced Cauliflower (Page 35), warmed
- Salt and pepper, to taste

INSTRUCTIONS

1. In a sauté pan, over medium heat, combine olive oil, lemon juice, seasoning mix, garlic, and parsley with the artichoke hearts; heat through.
2. Place arugula in the bottom of a bowl. Add warmed chicken and warmed riced cauliflower.
3. Position artichoke hearts as the next layer, then drizzle the warm olive oil dressing over the top of the bowl's content.
4. Salt and pepper, to taste.

CHAPTER ELEVEN

SANDWICHES

in this chapter

A sandwich is truly fantastic: It is not only portable, it is easy to pack, and perfect for meal planning. You can slap almost anything between two pieces of bread and call it a full meal. If you consume whole grains, use any of these recipes with whole-grain breads. However, if you are eating grain-free, no problem. Try one of the Smarty Pants Tortilla and Bread Substitute Ideas listed on Page 92 as a bread substitute.

TURKEY BURGERS
WITH LETTUCE BUNS

30 MINUTES

YIELDS 4 SERVINGS

I have slowly fallen in love with ground turkey; it's extra-lean and healthful. We have ground turkey in our household at least twice a week, and a good old-fashioned burger cooked with a modern twist is a great lunch or dinner choice. While I love this Cajun-flavored twist, you can swap the flavors to anything you prefer. Lettuce is great as a bun, and a thin layer of dairy-free mayo adds a bit of much-needed fat to bring it all together.

INGREDIENTS

Burger:
- 1 pound ground turkey
- 1 large egg, whisked
- 2 cloves garlic, minced
- 1 tablespoon minced fresh parsley
- 1 tablespoon Cajun Country Spice Seasoning Mix (Page 45)
- 1/2 teaspoon cayenne pepper
- Salt and black pepper, to taste
- 1 tablespoon oil

Toppings and Wrap:
- Whole leaves of lettuce
- Tomatoes, sliced
- Mayonnaise (soy-free, grain-free, dairy-free)
- Red onions, sliced thin

INSTRUCTIONS

1. In a large bowl, combine all the burger ingredients except the oil; mix well and form into equal sized patties.
2. In a skillet, heat oil to medium heat. Cook patties approximately 5 to 7 minutes per side, depending on thickness.
3. Serve with lettuce leaf "bun" and your toppings of choice.

OPEN-FACED GRILLED
PINEAPPLE BURGERS

30 MINUTES

YIELDS 4 SERVINGS

My first pineapple burger experience happened on a trip to Hawaii with my husband, Luis, when we were first married. Biting into a pineapple-laden burger is a sensational and flavor-filled experience. It makes your eyes close and your heart warm with happiness. Pineapple is brilliantly juicy when it's been grilled, so this open-faced sandwich needs no sauces or heavy toppings as the pineapple is the crowning glory for the burger. Great for summer picnics, lovely as an alternative for football season parties, and, of course, perfect for lunch.

INGREDIENTS

Burger:

- 1 pound ground meat (if you choose red meat, go with grass-fed)
- 1 large egg, whisked
- 1 tablespoon minced fresh parsley
- 1 tablespoon minced garlic
- 1 tablespoon grated ginger
- 1 teaspoon smoked paprika
- 1 teaspoon onion powder
- 1 teaspoon salt
- Salt and black pepper, to taste

Toppings and Wrap:

- 1 whole pineapple, peeled, cored, and sliced into rings
- Whole leaves of lettuce
- Sweet Vidalia or red onions, sliced thin

INSTRUCTIONS

1. Heat your grill or griddle to medium.
2. In a large bowl, combine all the burger ingredients; mix well and form into equal-sized patties.
3. Grill burgers to medium or desired doneness. Grill pineapple slices until slightly charred (approximately 5 minutes each side).
4. Serve burger with lettuce leaf "bun" or open faced with the pineapple slice on top.

CATER TO THE
'MATER BURGERS

30 MINUTES

YIELDS 4 SERVINGS

Tomatoes are so juicy and wonderful *inside* a sandwich, what about reversing that magic and putting them *outside* the sandwich? This recipe does just that. Top with grilled onions and the sandwich goes to off-the-hook flavor levels. I find these are absolutely charming as smaller "sliders." Use small tomatoes and small burgers for a big reaction from your friends and family.

INGREDIENTS

Burger:
- 1 pound ground turkey
- 1 large egg, whisked
- 1 large zucchini, grated
- 1 tablespoon minced shallots
- 1 tablespoon minced fresh basil
- 1 teaspoon minced garlic
- 1 teaspoon salt

Toppings and Wrap:
- Tomatoes, cut in half to use as a bun
- Whole leaves of lettuce
- Onions, grilled

INSTRUCTIONS

1. Heat your grill or griddle to medium.
2. In a large bowl, combine all the burger ingredients; mix well and form into equal-sized patties.
3. Grill burgers to medium or desired doneness.
4. Serve with tomato bun and toppings.

POTAYTO-POTAHTO
NUT BUTTER SANDWICHES

UP TO 25 MINUTES

YIELD VARIES

At one of my speaking events I met up with a little girl who has osteoarthritis in her elbow joints. She was in such pain. She and her mother discovered the anti-inflammatory food plan, and she has been doing much better. When she spoke with me, she said, "But I really miss peanut butter and honey sandwiches on white bread!"

I definitely understand that feeling, and this recipe leans toward the flavor for her and all you PB&H (or PB&J) lovers out there. I prefer to leave out the peanut butter because so many people are allergic or sensitive to peanuts. Enjoy!

INGREDIENTS

- Large sweet potatoes
- Sunflower seed butter
- Honey to drizzle, Smash Jam (Page 126), or fresh fruit

INSTRUCTIONS

1. Cut the large sweet potatoes in 1/2-inch thick slices. Toast 3 or 4 times, or roast in the oven for 20 minutes at 350 F.
2. Spread seed butter on the toasted slice, then top with a drizzle of honey, a dollop of jam, or a piece of fruit.

Adding freshly made tomato sauce to a homemade meatball sandwich or wrap is a way to make the zestiness level jump off the charts. This saves well for meal planning and leftovers. *Buon appetito!*

ITZ-ITALIAN
MEATBALL SANDWICHES

30 TO 35 MINUTES

YIELDS 8 SERVINGS

INGREDIENTS

Meatballs:

- 2 pounds ground chicken or turkey
- 2 eggs, whisked
- 1/2 cup coconut flour or cassava flour
- 1 1/2 tablespoons Mediterranean Lemon Seasoning Rub (Page 79) or Italian Seasoning Mix (Page 75)
- 1 tablespoon minced fresh parsley
- Salt and pepper, to taste
- 2 tablespoons olive oil

Sauce:

- 2 cups crushed tomatoes (canned or fresh)
- 1 tablespoon Italian Seasoning Mix
- 1 teaspoon crushed garlic
- 1/2 teaspoon salt
- Crushed black pepper, to taste

Toppings and Wraps:

- Leafy lettuce for wraps or as a topping
- Black olives, sliced thin

INSTRUCTIONS

For Meatballs:

1. Preheat oven to 350 F.
2. In a large bowl, combine chicken, eggs, flour, seasoning mix, parsley, salt, and pepper.
3. Roll mixture into 1-inch balls.
4. Heat oil in sauté pan to medium to high heat; cook meatballs until browned on sides.
5. Place meatballs on a baking sheet, and bake 20 to 25 minutes, or until completely done.

For Sauce:

6. In a saucepan, combine all ingredients, and cook over medium heat for 10 to 15 minutes.

To Assemble Sandwiches:

7. Place meatballs on lettuce wraps (or bread if you can have whole grains).
8. Top with sauce, then toppings, and serve.

CHAPTER TWELVE

SNACKS

in this chapter

Snacks are important to the success of an anti-inflammatory food plan; eating healthful snacks regularly helps keep blood sugar and protein levels even. Whether you have an inflammatory condition like diabetes or heart disease, or you have inflammatory pain from arthritis or another condition, keeping your sugar levels low and consistently even helps all inflammatory conditions. Lower sugar levels means lower inflammation.

Healthful snacks include protein-based foods such as nuts, seeds, beans, and other legumes. Another great snack idea is to consume treats with a lot of fiber. Studies have shown that increased fiber in your diet helps satiate you so you feel less hungry while reducing your cholesterol and blood pressure as well as your risk for heart disease.

I Wanna Glass O' Watah

We often feel "snacky" because we are bored or thirsty. Before you jump for an unhealthy food because you are feeling a bit snacky, first try drinking a single glass of water. Instead of being hungry, you may simply be thirsty; try it to see if it is thirst or hunger. This practice has me drinking healthier amounts of water and eating less junk.

Next, before snacking on something extra fatty or sugary, try eating raw vegetables. Eat with abandon because raw veggies can always be considered for a snack. If I feel "hungry or snacky" and it isn't dinner time yet, my nutritionist encourages me to eat as many raw vegetables as I would like to get me over the wait. Speak with your health professional and see if they agree for your specific health issues.

If you are traveling, the best idea is to pack your own snacks. Airports are notorious locations for unhealthy foods, and you can easily end up feeling sick and exhausted from eating foods that affect your inflammatory condition. Discover all kinds of snack ideas on the pages that follow.

VEGGIES
WITH NUT BUTTER

20 MINUTES

YIELDS 12 SERVINGS

Nut butters are great added to morning cereals, spread across grain-free bread, or just scooped up with a veggie. Once a week or so I get a craving for almond butter with celery. A serving is just a couple tablespoons, so I grab a big tablespoon and some celery and take a break in the afternoon with a good book. Fifteen minutes of veggie and nut butter therapy, and I feel ready to get back to work.

You can try all types of vegetables to dip; I prefer jicama, carrots, celery, and fennel. Once in a while I add some excitement and sprinkle a little cayenne or curry on the almond butter. You can make nut butter yourself—it only takes a bit of time and the result is creamy perfection.

INGREDIENTS

- 3 cups pecans, walnuts, or almonds
- Pinch of salt (optional)
- 2 teaspoons honey or maple syrup (optional)
- Jicama, carrots, celery, fennel, and zucchini, sliced into sticks

INSTRUCTIONS

1. Heat oven to 350 F.
2. To remove skins, blanch the nuts by boiling in water for 2 minutes (this is an optional step).
3. Place parchment paper on a baking sheet; spread all the nuts on the sheet in a single layer.
4. Roast for 5 to 8 minutes. Check often and do not burn the nuts. Remove the nuts from the oven and allow them to cool.
5. Add roasted nuts to a food processor, along with salt and honey, if using, and process for 10 minutes, scraping the sides frequently. Run for longer, if needed.
6. Store in an airtight glass container in the refrigerator. The nut butter will store for 3 to 4 weeks; stir before serving if the oil separates.

GARLIC NUT
SNACK ATTACK

30 MINUTES

YIELDS 12 TO 14 SERVINGS

The world is a better place because garlic is in our lives, am I right? I love to whip up a batch of these pecans and take them when I travel. They are perfect with a little club soda when I am on an airplane, and they make a fine afternoon savory snack as well at home or in your office. Want more garlic? Just add more. Want less salt? Just pull it out of the recipe. You are the chef in charge of your own snack attack.

INGREDIENTS

- 4 cups pecans (or any other nut you might like)
- 2 tablespoons extra-virgin olive oil
- 1 tablespoon Ranch Dressing Seasoning Mix (Page 49), or flavor swap another seasoning mix
- 1 teaspoon garlic powder
- 1 teaspoon salt

INSTRUCTIONS

1. Heat oven to 350 F.
2. In a large bowl, place all the ingredients, stirring well until all the nuts are evenly coated.
3. On a baking sheet covered in parchment paper, spread the coated nuts in a single layer.
4. Bake 15 to 20 minutes, or until golden brown.
5. Allow the nuts to cool before serving. Store in an airtight container at room temperature.

TACO NUTS & OLIVES
AS A SNACK

30 MINUTES

YIELDS 12 SERVINGS

Looking for strong flavors? I always keep fresh olives on hand as they are easy to find at the olive bars at many grocery stores—there are so many delicious varieties and I love them all. When I need a strong snack that is exciting and flavorful, I have a couple tablespoons of olives. Combined on an appetizer table or as an afternoon snack, olives and Taco Nuts are beautiful to look at, and both are spicy snacks that impress.

INGREDIENTS

- 3 cups nuts or seeds (your choice)
- 1 tablespoon extra-virgin olive oil
- 1 tablespoon Fajita Spice Seasoning Mix (Page 51)
- 1/2 teaspoon cayenne pepper (more if you like)
- 1/2 teaspoon salt

INSTRUCTIONS

1. Heat oven to 350 F.
2. In a large bowl, combine all the ingredients, stirring well until the nuts are evenly coated.
3. On a baking sheet covered in parchment paper, spread the coated nuts in a single layer.
4. Bake 15 to 20 minutes, or until golden brown.
5. Allow nuts to cool before serving. Store in an airtight container at room temperature.

CAULIFLOWER
POPCORN

65 MINUTES

YIELDS 4 SERVINGS

Cauliflower is so wonderful in all its forms—from cauliflower steaks to cauliflower rice to cauliflower pizza crust, this vegetable is super versatile. Cauliflower popcorn is another way to eat the vegetable. While it doesn't smell like traditional popcorn, it is super easy to pop the little florets in your mouth just like you would popcorn. I love it in the evenings during movie time with my hubby and a few friends as it gives me that "popcorn satisfaction" without all the grain drama.

INGREDIENTS

- 1 tablespoon extra-virgin olive oil
- 1 tablespoon dried parsley
- 1 teaspoon salt or flavored salt
- 1/2 teaspoon garlic salt (optional)
- 1 large head raw cauliflower, broken into small florets less than 1 inch wide

INSTRUCTIONS

1. Heat oven to 425 F.
2. In a bowl, whisk together oil, parsley, and salts. Drop in the cauliflower pieces and stir until all the pieces are well coated.
3. On a baking sheet covered with parchment paper, spread the cauliflower pieces in a single layer.
4. Bake 60 minutes, turning twice, until the cauliflower pieces are golden brown and caramelized (if you like crunchier pieces, bake for less time; if you like more tender pieces, bake for longer).
5. Serve immediately.

ROASTED TOMATO AND OLIVE
SHISH KEBABS

20 MINUTES

YIELDS 4 SERVINGS

Putting anything on shish-kebab skewers creates a memorable eating experience, and these cleverly roasted tomatoes and olives are colorful, flavorful, and aromatic. Perfect as a little snack treat for yourself or your guests, and outstanding as a predinner appetizer on a summer's evening.

INGREDIENTS

- 2 cups cherry tomatoes
- 2 cups mixed olives
- 2 tablespoons olive oil
- Salt and freshly cracked black pepper, to taste
- 3 tablespoons thinly sliced basil

INSTRUCTIONS

1. Place tomatoes and olives on skewers for grilling. Drizzle olive oil over tomatoes and olives and sprinkle with salt and pepper.
2. Grill for 5 to 10 minutes, flipping halfway through.
3. Place on a serving plate and immediately sprinkle with the basil.
4. Serve alone or with a grain-free tortilla.

GARLICKY
BRUSSELS SPROUT CHIPS

15 MINUTES

YIELDS 4 SERVINGS

As a little girl I would run terrified from my grandmother when she tried to get me to eat a single Brussels sprout. Seriously. Run. Terrified. Now I love everything about these green treasures from the garden and could easily eat them several times a week if they are roasted just right to release the best flavor. These little roasted nibbles are easy to prepare and taste brilliant. If you grew up as a doubtful Brussels sprout eater, give these chips a try; they will convert you, for sure.

INGREDIENTS

- 1 1/2 pounds large Brussels sprouts, ends trimmed off
- 2 tablespoons extra-virgin olive oil
- 1 teaspoon garlic powder
- Freshly cracked salt and black pepper, to taste

INSTRUCTIONS

1. Heat oven to 350 F.
2. Gently peel off the outer layers of each Brussels sprout, saving the hard inner core for another dish.
3. On a baking sheet covered with parchment paper, evenly spread out the layers of the sprouts.
4. Toss sprout layers with the olive oil and garlic powder, coating evenly while on the pan. Sprinkle with cracked salt and pepper.
5. Roast for 10 minutes (more if needed) until the leaves are brown and crispy.

GUACAMOLE
A LA MICHAEL

10 MINUTES

YIELDS 4 TO 6 SERVINGS

I will never forget the first time I had guacamole, it was a flavorful explosion of creamy goodness. It was also the first time I had ever tried avocado and—if you can imagine this—I was in my mid-20s. Back then avocados were not commonly found in central Indiana. Today, they are heaped in mountains in the produce section at the grocery store. Having grown up on a farm with limited exposure to the fruits of the world, I never even imagined that avocados could be so fabulous. Now I eat avocado several times a week and adore every bite.

When my friend Michael made his guacamole for me, he added a bit of kick with jalapeños—this elevated the flavor significantly. Thinly slicing an onion instead of dicing also provides a bit more crunch. It's a great recipe from a good friend. Thanks, Michael!

INGREDIENTS

- 2 or 3 ripe avocados, mashed with a potato masher or fork
- 1 handful of cilantro, minced
- 1 red onion, diced or sliced thin
- Juice of 1/2 lime
- 1 jalapeño, minced
- 1 tomato, diced
- Salt and pepper, to taste

INSTRUCTIONS

1. Combine all the ingredients, mixing well.
2. Serve with vegetables, grain-free chips (cassava chips are shown in the photo), or any grain-free tortilla or bread suggestions on Page 92.
3. Reserve one seed from the avocados and place it in any leftover guacamole to help prevent browning when storing it in the refrigerator. The guacamole only stores for about 24 hours, and the seed will help extend its freshness.

PART FOUR

DINNER MENU

Recipes that are fresh, delicious, and full of nutrition.

A challenging aspect of eating an anti-inflammatory evening meal is breaking old habits and building new ones. Traditional American home-cooked dinners are filled with meat and potatoes or pasta. I get it. That's what you ate growing up and what you are used to seeing on the table. Remember though, if you eat a lot of ultra-processed fast food, it is not good for your pain levels and medical conditions, because it can trigger inflammatory responses. That means you have to get out of those old habits of prepping food with high sugar and high carbohydrate levels, and into some new habits focused on healthful, anti-inflammatory whole foods.

We have talked about breakfast, lunch, and snacks, and the evening meal is equally important. The thing is, dinner can be complicated or you can make it super simple.

Let's say you don't want to cook a meal one evening—it's late, you are tired, you just want to sit in front of the television and enjoy some flat screen time. In Chapter 16, we'll take a look at what a standard meal plate looks like. Essentially the formula is this:

· *PRODUCE is half the plate: raw and cooked vegetables.*
· *PROTEIN is a quarter plate: protein of your choice.*
· *WHOLE GRAIN OR GRAIN-FREE CHOICE is a quarter plate: whole grains, starchy vegetables, or no-grain breads with healthful fat, all depending on your food sensitivities.*

With this formula in hand, redefine dinner. It doesn't have to look like it was cooked by Julia Child; your evening meal can occasionally be tossed together in five seconds flat—a pile of lettuce, a can of tuna, some beans or avocado, with a good dressing on top. That's it. Less than a few minutes to prepare and clean up. Quick. Easy. Manageable.

Don't be fooled into thinking that I sit around making large fancy meals with roasts every single day. I'm just like you—I have a busy life and I travel often. Sometimes I make a simple anti-inflammatory meal and enjoy it for what it is. Other days I spend a whole day meal prepping for the next week. The point being that eating an anti-inflammatory food plan is not hard; it is about reworking bad habits into healthier habits. One of the best places to start is your evening meal.

CHAPTER THIRTEEN

EASY MAIN DISHES

— *in this chapter* —

Anti-inflammatory main dish recipes feature zero grains, lots of whole foods, and very little processed foods. Most of these recipes can be prepared in advance and refrigerated or frozen, which makes them a perfect choice for meal planning and creation. Add these flavorful recipes to your collection and impress your family with full-on taste in food prepared from the heart.

BASIC GROUND
MEAT & VEGETABLE MIX

30 TO 45 MINUTES

YIELDS 8 SERVINGS

Have a house full of madness? I have the simple dinner answer—prepare a batch of precooked Basic Ground Meat & Vegetable Mix and keep it on hand for a super-quick addition to whatever your heart desires for dinner. Add it to tomato sauce, a stir-fry, soups, chili, or heat it up and serve it hot over the top of a fresh salad. So easy, and a smart timesaver.

INGREDIENTS

- 1 medium onion, diced
- 2 tablespoons extra-virgin olive oil
- 2 pounds ground turkey or chicken
- 1 package (16 ounces) frozen peas and carrots (or any other vegetables you prefer)
- 1 tablespoon any flavor swap seasoning mix
- Salt and cracked black pepper, to taste

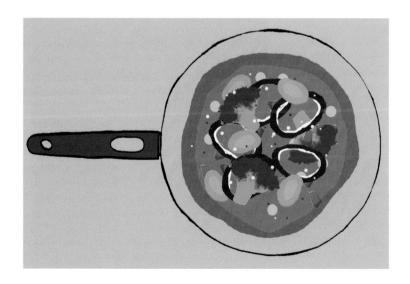

INSTRUCTIONS

1. In a large skillet, over medium heat, sauté the onion in the olive oil until it just starts to become transparent.
2. Add raw turkey, mixing in well.
3. Once mixture is cooked through, but not brown, add frozen vegetables. Add seasoning mix, salt, and pepper. Continue to brown in skillet until meat and vegetables are done, but not burned.
4. Serve as is or freeze in individual portions to pull out and add to chili, soups, vegetable stir-fries, or sauces.

Cooking pork in a slow cooker is the way to go. The slower cooking time breaks down the structure of the meat so it becomes incredibly tender. By cooking slowly all day, you are also enabling flavors to be absorbed by the meat. The recipe for cabbage leaf taco shells follows; they are a perfect balance with the flavorful pork meat (turn to Page 156 for a photograph of the shells). While reheating the cabbage shells means they will lose a bit of their crispiness, they still contain all the tastiness, and so can be easily used for advance meal planning. If you like, substitute with grain-free tortillas or another bread alternative (Page 92).

SLOW-COOKER PORK TACOS
WITH CABBAGE LEAF TACO SHELLS

UP TO 9 HOURS

YIELDS 8 SERVINGS

INGREDIENTS

Pork:

- 2 pounds pork roast or boneless pork chops
- 2 tablespoons Fajita Spice Seasoning Mix (Page 51)
- 2 cups meat or vegetable broth
- 1 large onion, sliced in strips
- 1 can (16 ounces) crushed or diced tomatoes
- 1/2 to 1 teaspoon cayenne pepper (optional)
- Salt

Cabbage Leaf Shells:

- 1 head cabbage, washed, cut in half, core removed
- 2 tablespoons extra-virgin olive oil
- Salt and cracked black pepper, to taste

INSTRUCTIONS

For the Slow-Cooker Pork:

1. Combine all pork ingredients in a slow cooker and cook on low for 6 to 8 hours. Pork will be falling-apart tender and ready to serve.

For the Cabbage Leaf Shells:

2. Heat oven to 400 F; line a baking sheet with parchment paper and set aside.
3. Gently pry cabbage leaves apart in either individual sheaths or with a few leaves piled on top of one another (they will curl up slightly on the sides).
4. Place on the prepared baking sheet; coat with olive oil and salt and pepper.
5. Roast for 30 to 40 minutes, until the edges are crispy, but not burned.
6. Serve fresh, slightly cooled, and use as "taco shells."

HERBED FLAVOR SWAP
PORK ROAST

2+ HOURS

YIELDS 8 TO 10 SERVINGS

This is the No. 1 requested dish in my household. My family loves this roast; the secret is to not overcook it as it needs to be tender and juicy for the most flavor. As a main course, this is beautiful sliced on a platter and served with salad and a side of Mashed Rutabaga (Page 197) or Ridiculously Delicious Roasted Root Vegetables (Page 195).

INGREDIENTS

- 1 tablespoon extra-virgin olive oil
- Salt and cracked black pepper, to taste
- 3 tablespoons Herbes de Provence Seasoning Mix (Page 77) or flavor swap another seasoning mix
- 3 pounds boneless pork

INSTRUCTIONS

1. Heat oven to 450 F. Place the oven rack in the center of the oven.

2. Combine olive oil, salt, pepper, and seasoning mix; rub mixture on the outside of the pork roast. Place in a roasting pan, fat side up.

3. Roast for 10 minutes, then (without opening oven) turn down the oven to 250 F.

4. Cook for another 50 to 90 minutes, or until the meat registers 150 F on a meat thermometer. Do not overcook or the pork will be dry.

5. Remove the roast, set on a cutting board, cover in foil, and allow it to rest for about 15 minutes. Slice and serve.

BEAUTIFUL BAKED
CITRUS SALMON

40 TO 45 MINUTES

YIELDS 4 TO 6 SERVINGS

Salmon is one of the easiest main courses to prepare; it is great alone with just salt and pepper, or, with only a few more ingredients, you can prepare an absolute work of art for dinner. Salmon is known as "brain food" as it is a particularly nutrient-dense fish filled with protein, vitamins, minerals, and omega-3 fatty acids. The salmon I purchase has had the skin and bones removed by my local fishmonger, and I love the leftovers for next-day salmon salads.

INGREDIENTS

- 1 large orange, cut in 1/4-inch slices
- 1 large lemon, cut in 1/4-inch slices
- 1 to 2 pounds salmon, skin and bone free
- 2 tablespoons extra-virgin olive oil
- Salt and cracked black pepper, to taste
- 1 tablespoon chopped fresh dill

INSTRUCTIONS

1. Heat oven to 400 F. Place the oven rack in the center of the oven.
2. Divide the citrus slices in half; place half of the slices on the baking sheet.
3. Rub both sides of the salmon with olive oil, then lightly salt and pepper both sides.
4. Lay the salmon on top of the citrus slices. Sprinkle fresh chopped dill over the top of the salmon. Lay the remaining citrus rounds on top of the salmon.
5. Bake the salmon, uncovered, for 25 to 30 minutes. The salmon should be completely cooked through at the thickest part, or until a meat thermometer registers 145 F.
6. Remove the salmon, slice, and serve immediately.

ROAST SPATCHCOCK
CHICKEN

80 TO 90 MINUTES

YIELDS 4 SERVINGS

A spatchcocked chicken is simply a chicken that has been butterflied. You remove the backbone entirely and lay the bird out flat on a baking sheet. This enables you to have a more evenly cooked chicken; an unevenly cooked chicken often happens when you leave it in whole form to roast. If you spatchcock a chicken it also takes less time to cook, which enables more moisture to be retained. In other words, to spatchcock a chicken is to prepare a deliciously moist and flavorful bird.

INGREDIENTS

- 1 chicken, about 4 pounds
- 1 tablespoon extra-virgin olive oil
- 3 cloves garlic, crushed
- 1 tablespoon Herbes de Provence Seasoning Mix (Page 77) or flavor swap another seasoning mix
- Salt and cracked black pepper, to taste

INSTRUCTIONS

1. Heat oven to 450 F. Place the oven rack in the center of the oven.
2. Lay the chicken on a cutting board, breast side down. Using kitchen shears or a sharp knife, cut out the backbone entirely. Spread open the chicken so you can see the ribs. Use a knife and slice down the middle of the sternum.
3. Flip the chicken over as you place it on a flat baking sheet; push hard on the skin side to flatten the chicken to the pan.
4. Rub with olive oil and garlic. Sprinkle with seasoning mix, salt, and pepper.
5. Roast with the skin side up for 45 to 60 minutes, or until the thigh meat registers 160 F on a meat thermometer.
6. Remove the chicken, set skin side up on cutting board, cover in foil, and allow it to rest about 5 minutes.
7. Slice into individual pieces and serve, store in the refrigerator, or package and place in the freezer.

ROTISSERIE CHICKEN
FAJITAS

30 MINUTES TO OVERNIGHT

YIELDS 4 SERVINGS

Tender, juicy, with a big flavor, these fajitas are quick to throw together since you don't cook the meat from scratch. I use rotisserie chicken meat as a way to make dinner prep a lot faster and easier. Organic rotisserie chickens are best, and, if you can't find organic, consider roasting whole organic chickens yourself as a part of your weekly food prep. This recipe is an adaptation of a very traditional recipe I love, and it is excellent with rotisserie chicken. Enjoy!

INGREDIENTS

- 1 whole rotisserie or roasted chicken
- 2 tablespoons olive oil
- 3 garlic cloves, crushed
- 2 tablespoons Fajita Spice Seasoning Mix (Page 51)
- Juice of 3 limes, divided
- 1 large onion, sliced thin
- 3 bell peppers, sliced thin
- 12 grain-free tortillas
- 2 tablespoons chopped cilantro
- 1 avocado, sliced thin
- Salt and pepper, to taste

INSTRUCTIONS

1. Remove chicken meat from bones, and slice into thin strips and shreds.
2. In a small bowl, create a marinade by combining the olive oil, garlic, seasoning mix, and the juice of 1 lime.
3. Combine onion and peppers with the marinade; allow to marinate for a few minutes to overnight.
4. Remove vegetables from marinade; sauté over medium-high heat until vegetables are tender and browned at the edges.
5. Add the chicken, mixing until heated through. Add juice of half a lime while cooking.
6. When done, remove mixture from heat.
7. Place fajita mixture on tortillas to serve; top with cilantro, avocado slices, remaining lime juice, salt, and pepper.

CHAPTER FOURTEEN

VEGETABLE SIDE DISHES

in this chapter

Every main dish needs a good side dish for variety and zest. Without both, our plates seem rather empty and bereft of excitement. The heart and soul of whole foods are the vegetables, and most side dishes are perfect when they include an assortment of vegetables. Using an anti-inflammatory food plan means your plate is typically half raw salad, and a cooked vegetable side dish definitely adds rich flavor to your meal.

Discover the perfect accompaniment to your next main dish with a few of these side dishes—all anti-inflammatory and filled with healthful happiness.

WHOLE BUTTERNUT SQUASH
IN A SLOW COOKER

6 1/2 HOURS

YIELDS 4 SERVINGS

Butternut squash is a perfect whole-food side dish. Using a slow cooker is an easy and hands-free way to make cooking tough-to-cut squash less stressful. This technique is particularly effective if you have lost strength in your hands and arms; raw butternut squash and pumpkin can be difficult to cut. Once it's cooked in the slow cooker, you can cut the squash like butter and it tastes fantastic. This technique works for any large squash or pumpkin.

INGREDIENTS

- 1 large butternut squash
  (a size that will fit your slow cooker)
- 1/4 cup water
- Drizzle of olive oil
- Salt and pepper

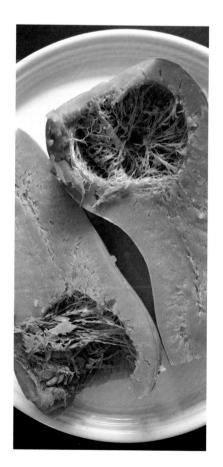

INSTRUCTIONS

1. Cut slits in the skin of the squash with a sharp knife.
2. Place squash in a slow cooker; add water. Turn to low and cook for 6 hours.
3. Remove from slow cooker when tender. Cut in half; remove seeds and discard.
4. Scoop out squash and discard rind.
5. Mash squash well. Mix in salt and pepper, drizzle with oil and serve, or refrigerate and save for other dishes.

SPAGHETTI SQUASH
LATKES

20 MINUTES

YIELDS 4 TO 6 SERVINGS

White potatoes have triggered my osteoarthritis pain for years. I have tried them every which way and have repeatedly suffered inflammatory consequences. In response to that, I have begun to find creative alternatives to all my favorite white potato dishes. This recipe includes a surprising ingredient—spaghetti squash. If you cut precooked spaghetti squash (Page 189 for the technique using the slow cooker) into rectangular shapes, then brown the outsides and salt lightly, it tastes very much like traditional latkes. Other types of squash taste too butternut-sweet or pumpkin-like; spaghetti squash has a neutral flavor. When you fry vegetables, they absorb the flavor of the fat used. This recipe is definitely higher in fat. I can eat this dish without an inflammatory reaction and enjoy it as a side dish for dinners and breakfasts.

INGREDIENTS

- 1 large spaghetti squash, cooked (Page 189 for technique using the slow cooker)
- 2 tablespoons extra-virgin olive oil
- Salt and pepper

INSTRUCTIONS

1. Allow cooked spaghetti squash to cool overnight in the refrigerator.
2. The next day, using a spatula and a knife, lift out a rectangle and set it on a plate. Continue cutting and shaping until you have several rectangles of squash. Keep the pieces thin; thicker pieces are less crispy.
3. Heat olive oil in a large frying pan on medium-high heat.
4. Sprinkle the top of a rectangle with salt and pepper, then place that side face down in the frying pan. Sprinkle the exposed side with salt and pepper.
5. Cook about 3 to 5 minutes, or until the bottom side is browned.
6. Flip over and continue cooking until the next side is browned.
7. Drain on a kitchen towel, and serve warm.

EXTREMELY GOOD CURRIED
CAULIFLOWER RICE

15 MINUTES

YIELDS 4 SERVINGS

Cauliflower rice is not rice, yet I find it has a consistency very similar to traditional white rice and I enjoy the flavor, so I eat it often. For years, I prepared this recipe without the curry, then one day I had an epiphany and tossed in a tablespoon of curry, and now I can't get enough. It is lovely with salmon or any main dish protein, and it also freezes well. If left to my own devices, I cook this several times a week purely for the flavor.

INGREDIENTS

- 1 batch Basic Riced Cauliflower (Page 35)
- 1 tablespoon Curry Spice Seasoning Mix (Page 55), add more if you like
- 1 tablespoon extra-virgin olive oil
- Salt and freshly cracked pepper

INSTRUCTIONS

1. Prepare riced cauliflower.
2. Heat olive oil in a large frying pan on medium heat. (I like using a cast-iron skillet for this.) Add riced cauliflower; sprinkle with seasoning mix, salt, and pepper. Stir fry until ingredients are well mixed and the dish is hot.
3. Serve with a main course.
4. Stores well in the refrigerator for a few days, or package for the freezer.

SUPER-DE-DUPER
VEGGIE STICKS

50 MINUTES

YIELDS 4 SERVINGS

Breading is, well ... bread. For a person trying to follow a grain-free food plan, a different type of breading can add crunch and a surprise taste. These veggies sticks have a high crunch factor and are fun to eat. Serve with marinara, a bit of soy-free mayonnaise, dairy-free ranch dressing, or just plain. Prepare a batch for football parties and neighborhood get-togethers, and your friends will never guess this is 100-percent grain-free.

INGREDIENTS

- 1 pound green beans, cut into 2-inch sticks
- 5 large egg whites, whisked
- 2 cups coarsely ground almond meal
- 2 tablespoons Ranch Dressing Seasoning Mix (Page 49)
- Salt and cracked black pepper, to taste
- 2 large yellow squash, cut into 2-inch sticks
- Olive oil cooking spray
- Marinara sauce or other dipping sauce (optional)

INSTRUCTIONS

1. If you want your beans to be less crispy, blanch before cooking.
2. Heat oven to 425 F. Line a baking sheet with parchment paper; set aside.
3. In a small bowl, whisk egg whites.
4. In another bowl, whisk together the almond meal, seasoning mix, salt, and pepper.
5. Dip each vegetable stick into the egg whites, and then into the almond flour mix. Move to prepared baking sheet.
6. Spray all sides lightly with cooking spray.
7. Bake for 30 to 40 minutes (watch carefully because they can burn quickly).
8. Serve plain or with sauce.

RIDICULOUSLY DELICIOUS ROASTED
ROOT VEGETABLES

UP TO 70 MINUTES

YIELDS 4 TO 6 SERVINGS

Root vegetables include taproots, bulbs, tuberous roots, corms, and anything in between—they are generally the part of the plant that lives underground and grows into large energy-storing, nutrient-dense organs. In fact, root vegetables are known to have a high concentration of antioxidants. You can grow root vegetables easily in most garden spaces with full sun. Once harvested, they are best stored in a cool, dark, dry larder, not touching one another. Touching encourages mold growth, so keeping them separated helps the vegetables last longer.

Some root vegetables such as daikon, radish, and jicama are mostly eaten raw. Other roots that are anti-inflammatory can also be cooked. These include beets, carrots, celeriac, garlic, kohlrabi, onions, parsnips, rutabagas, shallots, sweet potatoes, turnips, and yams. My favorite ways to cook root vegetables include roasting and grilling; both release the sweetness of the vegetables.

INGREDIENTS

- 1 1/2 pounds beets, peeled and cut into uniform 1-inch pieces
- 1 1/2 pounds carrots, peeled and cut into uniform 1-inch pieces
- 1 1/2 pounds yams, peeled and cut into uniform 1-inch pieces
- 2 tablespoons extra-virgin olive oil
- 2 tablespoons crushed garlic
- 1 tablespoon minced fresh rosemary
- Salt and crushed black pepper, to taste

INSTRUCTIONS

1. Heat oven to 425 F.
2. In a large bowl, place root vegetables, adding oil, garlic, rosemary, salt, and pepper. Toss until vegetables are evenly coated.
3. On 2 baking sheets or in baking dishes, spread root vegetables in a single layer. Do not crowd.
4. Roast root vegetables for 45 to 60 minutes. Check every 15 minutes until the vegetables are tender and can be easily pierced with a fork. Crispy or slightly blackened bits are desirable. Serve immediately.

ASPARAGUS & ONION
HASH

15 MINUTES

YIELDS 4 SERVINGS

As a grilled onion lover, I have found that onions give me a certain joy—right up there with garlic—and I often crave the savory flavor. Making a hash is trouble-free; you can cook up the hash while you prepare other things for dinner. Best yet, it always makes my home smell like the Queen's kitchen. Rotate the asparagus out and replace it with zucchini or red peppers, or whatever vegetable you are mad about and make an infinite variety of hash combinations.

INGREDIENTS

- 1 large onion, sliced thin
- 2 tablespoons extra-virgin olive oil
- 1 pound spring asparagus (or another favorite vegetable), cut into 1-inch pieces
- 2 tablespoons crushed garlic
- 1 tablespoon Italian Seasoning Mix (Page 75) or flavor swap another seasoning mix
- 1 teaspoon paprika
- Salt and crushed black pepper, to taste

INSTRUCTIONS

1. In a pan, on medium heat, sauté onion in olive oil until it starts to turn golden.
2. Add asparagus, continue to stir. Add garlic, seasoning mix, paprika, salt, and pepper; combine to evenly coat vegetables.
3. Cook until all veggies turn a dark golden brown.
4. Serve immediately.

SMISH-SMASHED
RUTABAGA

30 TO 40 MINUTES   YIELDS 4 TO 6 SERVINGS

White potatoes can be a trigger for inflammatory pain, but my heart and soul had a hard time eliminating mashed 'taters from my life. Rutabagas are a great way to find the consistency and creaminess of mashed potatoes while keeping the health benefits of anti-inflammatory foods. In fact, you can use cauliflower and almost any root vegetable to create a mashed dish, so experiment with this recipe and find which vegetables you love the most.

INGREDIENTS

- 1 to 2 large rutabagas
- Salted water
- 1 cup dairy-free milk
- 3 tablespoons crushed garlic (optional)
- Salt and cracked black pepper, to taste

INSTRUCTIONS

1. Wash rutabagas, peel, and cut into 2-inch chunks.
2. In a large stockpot, heat salted water over medium. Add vegetables and completely immerse them.
3. Reduce heat to medium-low and cover pot with a lid (watch to make sure water continues to simmer and bubble; if it does not, slightly increase the heat).
4. Simmer until a fork easily slides through a rutabaga piece. Drain, reserving 1/2 cup of the cooking liquid.
5. To cooked vegetables, add reserved liquid and dairy-free milk. If you want to add garlic, now is the time to do so.
6. Mash with a potato masher, add salt and pepper, to taste.
7. Serve immediately. Mashed rutabagas heat up well for leftovers, or package them for the freezer.

CHAPTER FIFTEEN

CASSEROLE & SOUP
RECIPES

---
in this chapter

Soups and casseroles prompt so many heart-and-soul memories from my childhood. While others choose to eat soup only in the colder months, I am a year-round soup fanatic. I love soup so much I could have it for breakfast, lunch, and dinner. Soups and casseroles ordered in restaurants typically contain heavy creams and cheese, and ultra-processed canned soups use grain flours to thicken sauces. All of those indulgent ingredients might make the casseroles and soups thicker, but they also elicit inflammatory reactions. An anti-inflammatory soup is free of heavy, grain-filled flour thickeners, pasta, and cream.

This chapter is filled with recipes with traditional tastes that are anti-inflammatory in a positive way.

HOW TO MAKE
HOMEMADE BROTH

DEPENDS ON AMOUNT OF WATER USED

Homemade broth is the richest addition to any soup. Whenever a soup recipe calls for water, I add broth instead, and it seems to elevate a soup to a higher plane of existence. This is a recipe for poultry broth; however, you can change it to a vegetable broth by substituting 2 pounds of mushrooms, leeks, and other vegetables or vegetable scraps for the meat.

Commercial broths are often filled with over-processed chemicals, so if you purchase boxed broth, get the organic version and check the ingredient list to make sure it is a product that is anti-inflammatory in nature.

INGREDIENTS

- 2 pounds poultry bones and chicken pieces (substitute 2 pounds mushrooms, leeks, or other vegetable scraps for an all-vegetable broth)
- 1 whole onion, pierced
- 2 large carrots, cut into chunks
- 2 large celery ribs, cut into chunks
- Onion skins and vegetable peels
- 2 rosemary stems
- 2 bay leaves
- 1 tablespoon black peppercorns

INSTRUCTIONS

1. Place all ingredients in a large stockpot. Fill with enough water to cover all ingredients.
2. Heat on high until fully boiling. Reduce heat to medium-low and cover the pot with a lid. Keep the simmer going for 3 to 5 hours.
3. Skim off any foam and discard.
4. Strain ingredients, saving any poultry meat for use in other recipes. If the broth is still cloudy, strain again with cheesecloth.
5. Allow liquid to cool in the refrigerator, then skim off the fat. (It's easier once the liquid has cooled.)
6. Store in the refrigerator for up to 5 days, or freeze for 6 to 12 months.

TURKEY VEGETABLE
CHILI

UP TO 7 HOURS

YIELDS 6 TO 8 SERVINGS

I love, love, love this turkey vegetable chili—I throw all the ingredients in a slow cooker before work, and dinner is ready with minimum fuss at the end of the day. This was my go-to easy meal when my children were little. This recipe is largely improvisational; add in whatever you have in the pantry and allow it to cook all day for an easy dinner. Want it to be vegan? Swap out the meat and put in extra vegetables and beans.

INGREDIENTS

- 1 pound ground turkey, cooked, or 1 pound Basic Ground Meat & Vegetable Mix (Page 179)
- 4 cups mixed vegetables
- 1 onion, chopped
- 1 can (28 ounces) crushed tomatoes
- 1 can (14.5 ounces) diced tomatoes
- 2 tablespoon Chili Spice Seasoning Mix (Page 46)
- 1 teaspoon cumin
- Cayenne pepper, to taste
- Salt and pepper, to taste
- Vegetable or chicken broth, enough to create desired soup consistency
- Sliced avocado, for garnish

INSTRUCTIONS

1. Combine everything in a slow cooker.
2. Cook on low 4 to 6 hours, adding more liquid if needed.
3. Serve with avocado slices.

GARLIC CHICKEN
SOUP

UP TO 2 1/2 HOURS

YIELDS 12+ SERVINGS

What happens when Mom gets sick? I have to fix my own darned soup, that's what. This soup is a step easier as it uses rotisserie chicken. I also keep some broth in my freezer at all times in case such an emergency arises. I've discovered that the garlic is critical to the healing process and makes this chicken soup rather extraordinary. Perfect for when Mom gets sick, or when the weather turns a bit chilly and I need a pick-me-up.

INGREDIENTS

- 2 tablespoons olive oil
- 3 cups chopped carrots
- 2 cups chopped celery
- 1 large onion, chopped
- 3 tablespoons crushed garlic
- 1 pound rotisserie or roasted chicken, shredded
- 2 boxes (32 ounces each) organic chicken stock, or 8 cups homemade broth
- 1 tablespoon Herbes de Provence Seasoning Mix (Page 77)
- 2 tablespoons chopped fresh parsley
- Salt and freshly cracked pepper, to taste

INSTRUCTIONS

1. In a stockpot, heat olive oil over medium heat, and sauté the carrots, celery, onion, and garlic until the onion begins to turn translucent.
2. Add chicken, broth, and the seasoning mix; stir well and bring to a boil.
3. Cover and reduce temperature to low; keep on a slow simmer for 1 to 2 hours.
4. Top each serving with fresh parsley, salt, and pepper. Serve hot.

PUMPKIN COCONUT
CURRY SOUP

90 MINUTES

YIELDS TO 8 SERVINGS

Curry soup is something new and exciting for my palate. I discovered it in a tiny Indian café in Asheville, North Carolina, and fell madly and truly in love. It can be made without meat, which makes it a great vegan option; if you want to add chicken broth or even chunks of chicken, it tastes wonderful as well. This soup can be made with added cayenne pepper for some extra spiciness. Either way, the flavors are rich and interesting.

INGREDIENTS

- 2 tablespoons extra-virgin olive oil
- 1 small onion, finely minced
- 2 cloves garlic, minced
- 2 teaspoons grated fresh ginger
- 2 teaspoons Curry Spice Seasoning Mix (Page 55)
- 1 1/2 teaspoons Pumpkin Pie Seasoning Mix (Page 91)
- 3 cups pumpkin purée (fresh or canned)
- 1 tablespoon maple syrup
- 4 cups chicken or vegetable stock
- 1 can (14 ounces) coconut milk
- Salt and cracked black pepper, to taste
- Chives or watercress and a little chili sauce, for garnish

INSTRUCTIONS

1. In a large stockpot, heat oil over medium-high heat and cook onion until clear.
2. Add garlic, ginger, and seasoning mixes; stir together to release aromas.
3. Stir in pumpkin and maple syrup, followed by stock. Bring mixture to a boil.
4. Cover and reduce heat to low; keep at a slow simmer for 1 hour. Then use an emulsion blender to blend mixture in the stockpot, or pour mixture in a blender and blend well. If using a blender, you may need to process the soup in batches.
5. Keep mixture on low heat or pour mixture back in pot and keep on low heat. Add coconut milk, and season with salt and cracked black pepper.
6. Serve with garnish.

CHICKEN BACON RANCH
CASSEROLE

60 MINUTES

YIELDS 4 SERVINGS

The easiest approach to making a creamy white sauce without dairy products is to add dairy-free ranch dressing. Too much dressing, however, and the casserole becomes too wet and will likely taste a bit vinegary. This casserole is creamy and flavorful without a hint of dairy, perfect if you are craving a traditional casserole. The hint of white sauce makes this dish rich and lovely. Fresh herbs are what takes this recipe up to the level of wonderful and yummy!

INGREDIENTS

- 1 pound rotisserie or roasted chicken, shredded
- 1 large onion, diced
- 1 batch (about 4 cups) Basic Riced Cauliflower (Page 35)
- 1 cup dairy-free mayonnaise
- 1 tablespoon Ranch Dressing Seasoning Mix (Page 49)
- 1 tablespoon apple cider vinegar
- 2 tablespoons dairy-free milk
- 8 strips bacon, fried and crumbled
- Salt and cracked black pepper, to taste
- Fresh herbs, for garnish

INSTRUCTIONS

1. Heat oven to 350 F.
2. Place chicken in a 9-by-11-inch casserole. Add onion and riced cauliflower.
3. In a small bowl, whisk together mayonnaise, seasoning mix, vinegar, and dairy-free milk.
4. Stir sauce into chicken mixture in casserole. Top with bacon crumbles, and season with salt and cracked black pepper.
5. Bake for 30 minutes, covered, then an additional 15 minutes uncovered.
6. Remove from oven, top with fresh herbs, and serve.

CHICKEN & APPLE
SAUSAGE CASSEROLE

35 MINUTES

YIELDS 4 SERVINGS

When making sausage dishes, I look for sausage without nitrites, monosodium glutamate (MSG), or other extras that might be inflammatory. Read the labels to find something as close to your food plan as possible, or go to a local butcher and have custom sausage made just for you. Some sausages are gluten- and grain-free while others are not. This casserole is quick to throw together and absolutely delicious.

INGREDIENTS

- 1 tablespoon olive oil
- 1 large onion, cubed
- 12 ounces chicken & apple sausage, sliced in rounds
- 4 cups cubed butternut squash or yams
- 1 tablespoon any flavor swap seasoning mix you prefer (I like Curry Spice Seasoning Mix, Page 55, or Herbes de Provence Seasoning Mix, Page 77)
- Salt and cracked black pepper, to taste

INSTRUCTIONS

1. Heat oven to 350 F.
2. Heat oil in a cast-iron skillet over medium heat.
3. Sauté onions and sausage until onion just turns translucent. Stir in butternut squash and seasoning mix, and season with salt and cracked black pepper.
4. Bake 15 to 25 minutes, or until ingredients begin to brown.
5. Remove from oven and serve.

CHAPTER SIXTEEN

MEAL PLAN GUIDE

What a Meal Plate Looks Like

In the photograph on the next page, you see a sample whole-food, anti-inflammatory plate. This gives you a rough idea of what your daily meal plates should look like although it is not a set-in-stone recommendation.

As was talked about in Chapter 13:

- *PRODUCE is half the plate: raw and cooked vegetables.*
- *PROTEIN is a quarter plate: protein of your choice.*
- *WHOLE GRAIN OR GRAIN-FREE CHOICE is a quarter plate: whole grains, starchy vegetables, or no-grain breads with healthful fat, all depending on your food sensitivities.*

Once you complete your initial 30 to 60 days of the food plan, try reintroducing whole grains and other foods into your diet one every four days. If they do not stimulate inflammatory responses in your body, then move forward with a meal plate plan that includes 100-percent whole grains. If not, use no-grain breads and various vegetables in the place of grains as a grain-free choice until your system will accept whole grains. Your health-care professional can guide you on the best personal practices for reintroducing foods.

After four years, I am still on a dairy-free and grain-free food plan because my body continues to react to grains and dairy as well as a few other foods. This is not a surprise, because dairy is known to be inflammatory for many individuals, and my health-care professionals specifically recommended I go off dairy permanently. I substitute with non-soy, non-dairy options when appropriate. Your health-care professionals may follow this recommendation or recommend you consume dairy moderately, only a couple times per week in small portions. If you can eat dairy, with your health-care professional's permission, I suggest you place it in the protein section of the above plate, but consume it sparingly. Taking allergy concerns and food sensitivities into account, I have made all the recipes in this cookbook grain- and dairy-free so the recipes readily conform to most healthy diet plans and anti-inflammatory food plans.

Too much of a good thing is a definite no-no in any food category. Using moderation in your diet helps keep inflammatory responses low. Eating a food plan high in whole foods and plant-based products, and low in red meat, processed foods, and sweets can truly make a difference for your level of health. Eating any foods in moderation is the best approach. The exception is raw, whole-food vegetables—eat in abundance!

The portion and serving sizes listed on the next page are not meant to be conformed to and measured out to perfection. Simply try to eat more vitamin-rich, plant-based foods, lean proteins, and healthy fats whenever possible, and use the list as a general guide for your meal plan.

SMART PORTION AND SERVING SIZE GUIDE

- Beans and other legumes: 1/2 cup cooked
- Dried fruit: 1/4 cup unsweetened; add 1 tablespoon juice to sweeten
- Eggs: 1 to 2 eggs
- Fresh fruit: 1/2 cup
- Healthy fats such as avocados, coconut meat, or olives: 1/4 cup
- Meat or fish: 1 cup

- Nut and seeds: 1/4 cup
- Oils: 1/2 to 1 teaspoon for each serving when cooking; 2 tablespoons for salad dressings; no more than 4 tablespoons in a day
- Vegetables, cooked or starchy: 1/2 cup
- Vegetables, raw: 2 cups or more
- Whole grains & non-grain breads: 1/2 cup cooked; a single slice of whole-grain bread; 1 tortilla

FEEL FULL ALL DAY!

Initially, your anti-inflammatory food plan will feel restrictive. Believe me, I understand how you feel. I suggest you make this effort to help build new habits that will lead to fewer chronic inflammatory issues. Experts say it takes 30 days to build a new habit, and you are doing just that by staying on your 30- to 60-day plan. Once you learn what a meal plate looks like, and you begin working with all kinds of new flavors, vegetables, and foods, then the food plan begins to feel less regulated, more flavorful, and easier to accomplish.

As you reintroduce foods and test your reactions, you will see you can still have some of your old favorites without any of the pain or gut discomfort you might have had before. Since you are reducing inflammation overall, some foods will no longer cause a problem. Meanwhile, you will begin to feel full regularly because you are consuming lots of plant-based food. Imagine a diet where you are less hungry all the time, while you can still eat and eat and eat? This is the whole-food anti-inflammatory plan.

The chart below illustrates what a typical day might look like while on your 30- to 60-day food plan. Moderation is the key to all things, and staying with moderate serving sizes means you will not overeat (see breakout serving size chart, Page 209). Of course, it helps to understand the amount that is healthy to eat. While it is best to have more than half your plate filled with vegetables, as an estimate, the standard-sized portion for proteins, whole grains, non-grain breads, fruit, and beans or other legumes is typically the size of your fist or smaller. This is just a rough estimate, but if you order chicken at a restaurant and half a chicken comes out, make a fist and hover it above your plate to get an estimate of what the serving size should really be.

DAILY MEAL PLAN FORMULA

BREAKFAST	LUNCH	DINNER	SNACK
PROTEIN	PROTEIN	PROTEIN	PROTEIN OR HEALTHY FAT
VEGETABLE AND/OR GRAIN / GRAIN-FREE	PRODUCE	PRODUCE	VEGETABLE
FRUIT	GRAIN / GRAIN-FREE	GRAIN / GRAIN-FREE	FRUIT OR GRAIN / GRAIN-FREE
BEVERAGE	HEALTHY FAT OR CONDIMENT	HEALTHY FAT OR CONDIMENT	BEVERAGE / WATER
	BEVERAGE	BEVERAGE	

A LAZY PERSON'S DINNER PREP OR HOW TO PREPARE EASY MEALS IN ADVANCE

News flash: When you prepare your meals in advance, you save time and money, and you help yourself successfully stay on a food plan. Buying in bulk means you spend less on food staples. If you plan your meals in advance, it means less impulse eating and less impulse buying of ultra-processed foods; you will go to the grocery story with goals for whole-food cooking and a specific prepared list.

Another benefit of meal prepping is better portion control. A prepped meal is a set meal. Your brain knows that when you finish your meal, you are done for that meal time. No extra food on your plate at the end of your meal means you managed your portions precisely.

Without a doubt, the best part of meal prepping is that you save time daily in preparing for and cleaning up after meals. Imagine coming home from work, popping in a quick meal, and heating it in less than five minutes. Super easy compared to spending a lot of time and effort every night of the week on dinner. According to the United States Department of Agriculture (USDA), women spend about six hours per week working up meals. With meal prepping, it is easy to spend less than three hours preparing food for the entire week for your entire family. All this makes meal prepping a smart addition to your food plan.

HOW TO MEAL PREP

Meal prepping might include making a full-sized meal for your family or breaking that down to individual meals for one person, then refrigerating or freezing these meals for future use. I prefer freezing advanced prepared meals because I am personally sensitive to molds. Refrigerating leftovers for more than 24 hours can encourage microscopic molds to grow on foods, causing a reaction in sensitive individuals. Freezing helps prevent mold growth and holds the meals safely for a longer period of time.

Some items do not advance prep well. For instance, crisp food like crackers will become mushy if refrigerated or frozen. Raw fruit such as apples and pears also do not do well when cut in advance. They usually brown up with air exposure, so it is better to store them cooked or wait to cut them into your dish just before consuming. Salad does not freeze well at all. Prepping everything but your salad for a meal makes sense; just prepare the salad portion at the last minute. To prevent overcooking when it is time to eat your food, choose recipes that can be enjoyed cold or can be gently reheated so the foods keep their taste and consistency.

Food containers are an important choice for meal prep. Plastics might be a concern for you as many plastic containers have carcinogenic BPA (bisphenol A) or estrogenic chemicals that leach into food. If you wrap everything in plastic wrap, plastic baggies, or place the food in plastic containers with snap-close lids, consider a healthier alternative such as glassware or stainless steel containers. Food in these containers can be scooped out and reheated in a pan; the glassware can also be microwaved.

Shop for all your ingredients the day before your meal prep day so the food is fresh. Plan meals centered on your health goals. Most importantly, create balanced meals with enough food to fill you up so you are not left hungry and wanting more.

Schedule time for your meal preparation; several hours on one day works well. A few dishes in the oven, one in the slow cooker, and one on the stove make for convenient multi-tasking. Once you are more experienced at meal prepping, consider prepping an entire month of different dishes in advance. This way you prepare a large variety of foods, and never have to repeat the same meal the next day.

FOOD SAFETY

Food safety is extremely important in the kitchen. Wash produce, your hands, your storage dishes, and all surfaces before and after prepping. Preventing contamination is a smart practice for food preparation, so purchase before "sell-by" or expiration dates, follow handling recommendations on packaging, and keep meat and poultry in its packaging until just ready to use. Keep frozen foods at zero F (-18 C). An important note: If freezing meat or poultry in the original packaging, consider placing in a freezer bag or wrapping in heavy-duty foil before placing the food in the freezer. For a guide to safe refrigerator and freezer storage, review the chart on the following pages.

	PRODUCT	REFRIGERATOR	FREEZER
	EGGS		
	Fresh, in shell	3 to 5 weeks	don't freeze
	Raw yolks, whites	2 to 4 days	1 year
	Hard-cooked	1 week	don't freeze
	Liquid pasteurized eggs or egg substitutes, opened	3 days	don't freeze
	Liquid pasteurized eggs or egg substitutes, unopened	10 days	1 year
	CASSEROLES & SOUPS/STEWS		
	Casseroles	1 day	3 to 4 months
	Soups with vegetables or meat-added & mixtures of both	3 to 4 days	2 to 3 months
	DELI & VACUUM-PACKED PRODUCTS		
	Store-prepared (or homemade) egg, chicken, tuna, ham, macaroni salads	3 to 5 days	don't freeze
	FISH & SHELLFISH		
	Lean fish (bass, catfish, cod, flounder, grouper, haddock, halibut, mahi-mahi, monkfish, orange roughy, perch, shark, sole, swordfish, tilapia, trout, tuna)	1 to 2 days	6 to 8 months
	Fatty fish (Chilean sea bass, anchovies, carp, herring, mackerel, salmon, sardines)	1 to 2 days	2 to 3 months
	Cooked fish	3 to 4 days	4 to 6 months
	Smoked fish	14 days	2 months
	Fresh shrimp, scallops, crawfish, clams, mussels, oysters, squid	1 to 2 days	3 to 6 months
	Canned seafood (in pantry, up to 5 years)	after opening 3 to 4 days	out of can 2 months
	BACON & SAUSAGE		
	Bacon	7 days	1 month
	Sausage, raw .from pork, beef, chicken, turkey	7 days	1 to 2 months
	Smoked breakfast links, patties	7 days	1 to 2 months
	FRESH MEAT (BEEF, VEAL, LAMP, PORK, GAME)		
	Steaks	3 to 5 days	6 to 12 months
	Chops	3 to 5 days	4 to 6 months
	Roast	3 to 5 days	4 to 12 months
	Variety meat (tongue, kidneys, liver, heart, chitterlings)	1 to 2 days	3 to 4 months

	PRODUCT	REFRIGERATOR	FREEZER
MEAT LEFTOVERS			
	Cooked meat & meat dishes	3 to 4 days	2 to 3 months
	Gravy & meat broth	1 to 2 days	2 to 3 months
RAW HAMBURGER, GROUND MEAT, & STEW MEAT			
	Hamburger & stew meat	1 to 2 days	3 to 4 months
	Ground turkey, veal, pork, lamb	1 to 2 days	3 to 4 months
FRESH POULTRY			
	Whole	1 to 2 days	1 year
	Chicken or turkey, parts	1 to 2 days	9 months
	Giblets	1 to 2 days	3 to 4 months
COOKED POULTRY, LEFTOVERS			
	Fried chicken & rotisserie chicken	3 to 4 days	4 months
	Cooked poultry dish	3 to 4 days	4 to 6 months
	Pieces, plain	3 to 4 days	4 months
	Pieces, covered with broth, gravy	3 to 4 days	6 months
	Chicken patties	3 to 4 days	1 to 3 months
FRUIT			
	Apples, peaches, pears	2 to 6 weeks	4 to 6 months
	Avocados, bananas	1 to 2 days	1 to 3 months
	Berries & grapes	1 to 2 weeks	10 to 12 months
	Citrus fruit	2 to 6 weeks	4 to 6 months
	Pineapple	6 to 9 days	10 to 12 months
	Tomatoes (overripe or sliced)	3 to 7 days	2 months
VEGETABLES			
	Artichokes, eggplant	3 to 7 days	6 to 8 months
	Asparagus, rutabagas, turnips	2 to 3 days	8 to 10 months
	Bamboo shoots, cabbage, celery, cucumbers, endive, radishes, salad greens, watercress	3 to 7 days	don't freeze
	Beans, beets, bok choy, broccoli, Brussels sprouts, carrots, cauliflower, greens, spinach, squash	3 to 5 days	10 to 12 months

ACKNOWLEDGMENTS

Special thanks go to my dear husband and daughters who put up with the drama of my passionately writing a book that means so much to me: I love you!

Many special thanks to Deepa Deshmukh, my nutritionist and guru in all things anti-inflammatory who helped me rediscover my health and mobility. She has reviewed and approved the basic anti-inflammatory ideas in this book and lives the lifestyle she encourages. I am grateful for your knowledge and friendship, Deepa; thank you from the bottom of my heart.

Books cannot become books without an entire team. My editor, Jean Teller, has been a joy to work with on this project as she understands my vision. She is generously kind and has helped me be a better cookbook author and photographer. Thanks to the lovely team at Ogden Publishing—from graphic designers to marketers to salespeople to editors to managers—who have believed in me and worked behind the scenes tirelessly to help this book move forward.

Several of the illustrations were created by Kelsey Lee Connors; thank you for your creative design. Thanks go to The Garden Sisters and my dear Level-Up Beta Team for helping me stay real. Thanks to Jenny Nybro Peterson, Terri Curtis, and Jacque Gregory for allowing me to include their yoga superpowers in the book's images. Thanks to Sheila Rutledge from Captured by Sheila for the photos of me on the back cover and at the beginning of the book. Thanks go out to Lisa Ziegler, Frank Hyman, and my niece Samara Sears, who all inspired me at a time I needed a real kick in the butt. You are appreciated so very much.

I would be remiss if I did not mention all the amazing people who speak with me every day on social media. You are my friends—you come to my speeches, order my books, and encourage me in ways I could have never imagined. When I first started walking daily, all of you lovely people cheered me on. You have seen my transition from extreme pain to a lifestyle filled with less pain and a lot of promise. I am so very, very happy to have each and every one of you in my life.

Please remember that I BELIEVE IN YOU, and I am grateful for you. If I can turn my health around through a wellness lifestyle, you can too. Life begins at the end of your comfort zone—go out there and conquer inflammation and live a wellness lifestyle!

MEASUREMENT CONVERSION CHARTS

Tsp	Tbsp	Cup	Pint	Quart
1/4	-	-	-	-
1/2	-	-	-	-
1	1/3	-	-	-
3	1	-	-	-
6	2	1/8	-	-
12	4	1/4	1/8	-
24	8	1/2	1/4	1/8
48	16	1	1/2	1/4
96	32	2	1	1/2
192	64	4	2	1

Liquid Measures				
1 teaspoon	-	1/3 tablespoon	5 ml
1 tablespoon	1/2 fluid ounce	3 teaspoons	15 ml, 15 cc
2 tablespoons	1 fluid ounce	1/8 cup, 6 teaspoons	30 ml, 30 cc
1/4 cup	2 fluid ounces	4 tablespoons	59 ml
1/2 cup	4 fluid ounces	8 tablespoons	118 ml
3/4 cup	6 fluid ounces	12 tablespoons	177 ml
1 cup	8 fluid ounces	1/2 pint/16 tablespoons	237 ml
2 cups	16 fluid ounces	1 pint/32 tablespoons	473 ml
4 cups	32 fluid ounces	1 quart	946 ml
8 pints	128 fluid ounces	1 gallon	3,785 ml, 3.78 liters
1 liter	-	1.057 quarts	1,000 ml

Dry Measures			
1 ounce	-	30 grams (28.35 g)	-
2 ounces	-	55 grams	-
3 ounces	-	85 grams	-
4 ounces	1/4 pound	25 grams	-
8 ounces	1/2 pound	240 grams	-
12 ounces	3/4 pound	375 grams	-
16 ounces	1 pound	454 grams	-
32 ounces	2 pounds	907 grams	-

courtesy Le Melange LLC, www.lemelange.com

WEIGHT

U.S.	Metric
1/2 oz	14.17 g
1 oz	28.35 g
1/4 lb	113.40 g
1/3 lb	149.69 g
1/2 lb	226.80 g
3/4 lb	340.19 g
1 lb	453.59 g

TEMPERATURES

	Fahrenheit	Celsius	Gas Mark
Freeze	32 F	0 C	-
Boil	212 F	100 C	-
Bake	325 F	165 C	3
-	350 F	180 C	4
-	375 F	190 C	5
-	400 F	200 C	6
-	425 F	220 C	7
-	450F	230 C	8
Broil	-	-	Grill

VOLUME

U.S.	Milliliters	Fluid Oz
1/4 tsp	1.25	-
1/2 tsp	2.5	-
1 tsp	5	-
1 Tbsp	15	1/2
2 Tbsp	30	1
1/4 cup	60	2
1/2 cup	120	4
1 cup	240	8
1 quart	1 liter	32

PAN SIZES

8X8-inch baking dish	20X20-centimeter dish
9X13-inch baking dish	22X33-centimeter dish
9-inch cake pan	22-centimeter pan
10-inch cake pan	25-centimeter pan
9X5-inch loaf pan	23X12-centimeter pan

SPECIAL PRODUCTS AND FOODS USED IN THIS BOOK AND WHERE TO FIND THEM

Food
• *Grain-Free:* Bob's Red Mill, www.bobsredmill.com
• *Lentil Krispies* (bottom left photo): Nutritionist Deepa's website, www.nutritionistdeepa.com

Herbs, Salts, & Spices
• Frontier Co-op, www.frontiercoop.com
• Mountain Rose Herbs (all the salts in the book are from MRH), www.mountainroseherbs.com
• Simply Organic, www.simplyorganic.com

Kitchen Tools
• *Adjustable Slicer w/Julienne Blade:* Microplane, www.us.microplane.com (bottom right photo)
• *Ceramic Knifes:* Kyocera Kitchen, www.kyoceraadvancedceramics.com
• *Cutting Board:* Totally Bamboo, www.totallybamboo.com
• *Dishes:* Many dishes in this book are from Fiestaware of the Homer Laughlin Co.,
  www.fiestafactorydirect.com
• *Flexible Cutting Mats:* Kyocera Kitchen, www.kyoceraadvancedceramics.com
• *Ginger Tool Grater:* Microplane, www.us.microplane.com
• *5 Blade Herb Scissors:* Crate and Barrel, www.crateandbarrel.com
• *Mortar & Pestle:* Cole & Mason USA, www.coleandmasonusa.com
• *Oil & Vinegar Pourer:* Cole & Mason USA, www.coleandmasonusa.com
• *Poptop Sealable Drinking Jar Lid:* Ecojarz, www.ecojarz.com (bottom right photo)
• *Salad Knife and Salad Hands:* Totally Bamboo, www.totallybamboo.com (bottom right photo)
• *Salt & Pepper Grinders:* Cole & Mason USA, www.coleandmasonusa.com

INDEX

INDEX

INDEX

INDEX

MEET SHAWNA CORONADO

Shawna Coronado is a wellness and anti-inflammatory lifestyle advocate who lives and gardens in the American Southwest. As an author, photographer, and media host, Shawna campaigns globally for social good and health awareness. With a make-a-difference focus on sustainable home living, organic gardening, and healthy anti-inflammatory living, she hopes to stimulate positive changes for chronic pain sufferers and people seeking an active wellness lifestyle.

Her food, garden, and eco-adventures have been featured in many media venues including radio and television. Shawna's successful organic living photographs and articles have been shown both online and off in many international food, home, and garden magazines and multiple books.

If you want to discover more of her organic, green, and ground-breaking books on living a wellness-centered lifestyle, or to sign up for Shawna's online courses, membership site, and newsletter, please connect online at www.shawnacoronado.com.